Open-Book Testing: Why It Makes Sense

By Kay Burke, Ph.D.

Educators who allow students to take open-book tests are not teaching *for the test*; they are teaching *for understanding.* Most students agree that open-book tests are more challenging than traditional objective tests because they require high-order thinking skills rather than recall skills.

The greatest benefit from open-book testing may be that it encourages the type of thinking that will benefit students in the real world.

- Open-book tests focus on students learning important concepts rather than memorizing facts.

- They encourage students to utilize the lifelong learning skill of "accessing information" rather than memorizing data. In most jobs, people do not have to memorize formulas or discrete bits of data; they have to know how to find the important information they need in order to solve problems and complete projects.

- Open-book tests encourage students to highlight the text and organize their notes so they can find the information they need.

- Open-book tests encourage students to **apply** the information they have learned and **transfer** it to new situations, rather than just repeat the facts.

Sources:

Burke, K.B. *The mindful school: How to assess authentic learning*. Arlington Heights, IL. Skylight Professional Development.

Stiggins, R.J. (1985, October). *Improving assessment where it means the most: In the classroom.* Educational Leadership, pp. 69-74.

Wiggins, G. (1989, April). *Creating tests worth taking*. Educational Leadership, pp. 121-127

Wiggins, G., & McTighe, J. (1989). *Understanding by design*. Alexandria, VA: Association for Supervision and Curriculum Development.

Test Bank

for

Beebe and Beebe

Public Speaking
An Audience-Centered Approach

Sixth Edition

prepared by

Ann Marie Jablonowski
Owens Community College

PEARSON

Boston   New York   San Francisco
Mexico City   Montreal   Toronto   London   Madrid   Munich   Paris
Hong Kong   Singapore   Tokyo   Cape Town   Sydney

ISBN 0-205-46822-5

Printed in the United States of America

10 9 8 7 6 5 4 3 2 1   10 09 08 07 06 05

Contents

Chapter 1 Speaking with Confidence

1) Having the resources, information, and attitudes that lead to action in achieving a desired goal is

   A) an action plan.
                      B) empowerment

   C) self–confidence.
                     D) organization.

Answer: B
Page Ref: 2
Topic: Why study public speaking?
Skill: Definition Question

2) The form of communication which is planned and more formal, with clearly defined roles, is called

   A) writing.
                      B) conversation.

   C) public speaking.
                   D) journaling.

Answer: C
Page Ref: 4
Topic: Public speaking & conversation, public speaking is formal
Skill: Definition Question

3) Translating ideas and images in the speaker's mind into verbal or nonverbal messages that an audience can understand is termed

   A) feedback.
       B) decoding.
       C) encoding.
       D) listening.

Answer: C
Page Ref: 6
Topic: Communication as action, source
Skill: Definition Question

4) When listening to a speech, an audience member translates the verbal and nonverbal messages into ideas, images and information through the process of

   A) receiving.
       B) hearing.
       C) believing.
       D) decoding.

Answer: D
Page Ref: 6
Topic: Communication as action, receiver
Skill: Definition Question

5) What is the term for something that interferes with the communication process?

   A) encoding.
                      B) decoding.

   C) channel confusion.
                 D) noise.

Answer: D
Page Ref: 6
Topic: Communication as action, noise
Skill: Definition Question

6) The most recent communication model focuses on two-person communication where messages are sent and received concurrently. This model is known as

    A) communication as action.   B) communication as interaction.

    C) communication as transaction.   D) communication as context.

Answer: C
Page Ref: 7
Topic: Communication as transaction
Skill: Definition Question

7) This is an older, more historical term used for communication that focuses on peoples efforts to use words and symbols to achieve their goals.

    A) lecturing.   B) imagery.   C) rhetoric.   D) decoding.

Answer: C
Page Ref: 7
Topic: The rich heritage of public speaking
Skill: Definition Question

8) This is the 19th-century practice of delivering an already-famous speech, rather than developing an original address.

    A) declamation   B) interpretation   C) oration   D) elocution

Answer: A
Page Ref: 8
Topic: The rich heritage of public speaking
Skill: Definition Question

9) If you have a normal or generally positive approach to communicating in public, where your heart rate is in the average range, what style of communication apprehension are you experiencing?

    A) average style   B) insensitive style

    C) inflexible style   D) confrontation style

Answer: A
Page Ref: 12
Topic: Understand your nervousness
Skill: Definition Question

10) According to several recent studies quoted in your text, the most important skills employers are seeking in college graduates are

    A) enthusiasm and work experience.

    B) good speaking and presentation skills

    C) technical and competence in the work area.

    D) attractive appearance and poise.

Answer: B
Page Ref: 3
Topic: Why study public speaking?
Skill: Description Question

11) One way public speaking and conversation are similar is that both are

    A) formal.   B) planned.

    C) audience-centered.   D) less fluid.

Answer: C
Page Ref: 4
Topic: Public speaking & conversation, public speaking is formal
Skill: Description Question

12) Noise in the communication process

    A) encodes the ideas.   B) can be external or internal.

    C) is the source of a message.   D) provides a channel.

Answer: B
Page Ref: 6
Topic: Communication as action, noise
Skill: Description Question

13) When we concentrate on what a speaker says and how it is said, we are

    A) concentrating on the source.

    B) encoding the content.

    C) engaging in feedback.

    D) focusing on the message or the speech itself.

Answer: D
Page Ref: 6
Topic: Communication as action, message
Skill: Description Question

14) A speaker transmits a message through two channels:

    A) visual and nonverbal.   B) voice and inflection.

    C) visual and auditory.   D) auditory and eye contact.

Answer: C
Page Ref: 6
Topic: Communication as action, channels
Skill: Description Question

15) The environment or situation in which a speech occurs is known as

    A) feedback.   B) a channel.

    C) communication.   D) context.

Answer: D
Page Ref: 6
Topic: Communication as interaction, context
Skill: Description Question

16) Students of 19th-century public speaking practiced the art of declamation which meant that they
    A) studied and applied arguments from famous documents.
    B) focused on posture, movement, gestures, and voice.
    C) spoke out vigorously against current political issues.
    D) delivered already-famous addresses of Patrick Henry and Edmund Burke.

Answer: D
Page Ref: 7-8
Topic: The rich heritage of public speaking
Skill: Description Question

17) When speakers tense and relax their muscles while waiting for their turn to speak, without calling attention to what they are doing, this reflects a strategy of coping with nervousness your text refers to as
    A) speech visualization.   B) adapting to the speaking environment.
    C) channeling your nervous energy.   D) speech preparation.

Answer: C
Page Ref: 15
Topic: Develop & deliver well-organized speech, nervous energy
Skill: Description Question

18) Speakers with a formal, planned speech, who can adapt and make decisions on the spot, indicate which of the following?
    A) The extra work a speaker puts in planning for every possible situation.
    B) Speakers adapt to their audience through audience-centered activity.
    C) They don't prepare everything and usually throw things in to fill time.
    D) A formal, planned speech is too confining for the speaker.

Answer: B
Page Ref: 4
Topic: Public speaking & conversation, public speaking is formal
Skill: Example Question

19) During a speech, an audience member stands up and asks a question, to everyone's surprise. According to your text, is the audience member's behavior appropriate?
    A) Yes; question and answer sessions are quite common in public speaking.
    B) No; the audience member should have remained seated to ask his or her question.
    C) No; the audience member did not maintain clearly defined roles of speaker and listener.
    D) Yes; in this day and age of informality, speakers should expect audiences to respond out loud.

Answer: C
Page Ref: 4-5
Topic: Roles of public speakers and audiences are clearly defined
Skill: Example Question

20) During the first day of speeches you had a bad sinus infection and your ears were plugged so you couldn't hear the speakers. You were experiencing

A) physical noise.

B) physiological noise.

C) psychological noise.

D) pseudo noise.

Answer: B
Page Ref: 6
Topic: Communication as action, noise
Skill: Example Question

21) Smiles, head nods, eye contact, and clapping from audience members are all forms of

A) encoding.   B) decoding.   C) internal noise.   D) feedback.

Answer: D
Page Ref: 6
Topic: Communication as interaction, feedback
Skill: Example Question

22) The instructor sees his students slouching in their seats, yawning, and doodling in their notebooks. The instructor reads the cues and adjusts his lecture accordingly. Which model of communication is presented here?

A) Communication as transaction.

B) Communication as interaction.

C) Communication as action.

D) Communication as context.

Answer: A
Page Ref: 7
Topic: Communication as transaction
Skill: Example Question

23) In a recent speech competition, students were asked to give an already-famous address from Martin Luther King, Jr., President John F. Kennedy, or President Ronald Reagan. These presentations, from a 19th-century perspective, would be considered the art of

A) oral interpretation.

B) declamation.

C) rhetoric.

D) public speaking.

Answer: B
Page Ref: 8
Topic: The rich heritage of public speaking
Skill: Example Question

24) The rhetoric of diversity refers to a speaker

A) considering how a setting can effect the message.

B) considering such factors as culture, ethnicity, and gender.

C) considering how one can use a variety of support.

D) considering such factors as education and experience.

Answer: B
Page Ref: 10
Topic: Public speaking & diversity
Skill: Example Question

25) Most speakers who procrastinate in preparing their speeches

    A) will sound much more spontaneous and relaxed.

    B) will be assured that the speech content is current and fresh.

    C) will feel more speaker apprehension.

    D) will be more interested in the topic.

Answer: C
Page Ref: 13-14
Topic: Build your confidence, don't procrastinate
Skill: Example Question

26) Tom is running for Student Government President. Because he has previously taken a public speaking course, he is able to speak with confidence, conviction, and assurance. Tom is experiencing

    A) speech effectiveness.   B) self-confidence.

    C) ego centrism.   D) empowerment.

Answer: D
Page Ref: 2
Topic: Why study public speaking? empowerment
Skill: Application Question

27) In his speech about volunteering for the American Red Cross, Jacob used a lot of slang words, sat and leaned on the table in front of the class, and was dressed very casually. Which of the following statements best describes this situation?

    A) Jacob adapted to his audience by making his speech more informal.

    B) Jacob violated the audience's space by sitting and leaning on the table in front of class.

    C) Jacob ignored the rule that public speaking is more formal than conversation.

    D) Jacob did nothing wrong by approaching this topic in a casual manner.

Answer: C
Page Ref: 4
Topic: Public speaking & conversation, public speaking is formal
Skill: Application Question

28) Joyce was going to her Anatomy and Physiology lecture. Before getting to class, Joyce received a call from the auto repair shop saying her vehicle would cost $729 to repair; money she didn't have. During the lecture she kept thinking about how she would pay for the repair. What type of noise was Joyce experiencing?

    A) external noise   B) physiological noise

    C) psychological noise   D) pseudo noise

Answer: C
Page Ref: 6
Topic: Communication as action, noise
Skill: Application Question

29) The speaker spoke so softly that audience members were straining to hear. They tried signaling the speaker by cupping their ears and giving a "thumbs up" sign to encourage the speaker to increase the volume. Finally, someone from the back of the room shouted, "Louder please!" Which of the following statements best describes this situation?

   A) The speaker ignored the context for the communication event.

   B) The speaker had decoding difficulties, while the audience had encoding difficulties.

   C) The source–receiver transaction experienced internal noise.

   D) The speaker ignored important audience feedback.

Answer: D
Page Ref: 6
Topic: Communication as interaction, feedback
Skill: Application Question

30) In her speech about lasik eye surgery, Shauna brought in a video showing a close up of an eyeball during surgery. Most of the class turned away from the video and stated their discomfort. Shauna was focused on her speech and didn't notice her audience. Which of the following best describes the situation?

   A) An effective public speaker should focus on both the message and the audience hearing it.

   B) An effective public speaker needs to grasp and keep the attention of the audience.

   C) An effective public speaker should focus on the message and visual aid without being distracted by external noise.

   D) An effective public speaker needs to be focused on the message because the audience will not follow along otherwise.

Answer: A
Page Ref: 7
Topic: Communication as transaction
Skill: Application Question

31) Dolores was asked to present her recent research findings to the XYZ Company. Because the response was so great, there would be a speech in the morning and one in the afternoon. At the 9:00 a.m. presentation the audience was attentive and asked insightful questions. However, with the same information presented at 1:00 p.m., the audience was quiet and lifeless. What aspect of public speaking had not been considered by Dolores?

   A) A speaker must consider feedback.

   B) A speaker must focus on visual and auditory channels.

   C) A speaker must consider the context of the speech.

   D) A speaker must acknowledge internal and external noise.

Answer: C
Page Ref: 6-7
Topic: Communication as interaction, context
Skill: Application Question

32) Wade took a public speaking class to help polish his presentation skills. However, the closer his time came to speak, the more nervous he felt. His heart was beating faster, his knees were shaking, his hands were beginning to sweat, and he was sure he would forget everything he had planned on saying. Which of the following best reflects what Wade experienced?

    A) Although Wade said he was ready to speak it's obvious he hadn't planned thoroughly enough.

    B) Wade was focused on the message and not the setting.

    C) Wade was experiencing a form of communication apprehension and anxiety common to public speakers.

    D) Wade had taken too many deep breaths before getting up to speak and was hyper-ventilating.

Answer: C
Page Ref: 11
Topic: Understand your nervousness
Skill: Application Question

33) Public speaking is sometimes called "the language of leadership."

Answer: TRUE
Page Ref: 2
Topic: Why study public speaking? empowerment

34) Employers are looking for individuals who have strong speaking and writing skills, more so than technical competence and work experience.

Answer: TRUE
Page Ref: 3
Topic: Why study public speaking? Employment

35) Public speaking is more formal and planned with clearly defined speaker and listener roles.

Answer: TRUE
Page Ref: 4
Topic: Public speaking & conversation, public speaking is formal

36) Messages are usually transmitted from sender to receiver through source and receiver channels.

Answer: FALSE
Page Ref: 6
Topic: Communication as action, channels

37) Speakers should focus on the message they are expressing more so than how the audience is responding to the message.

Answer: FALSE
Page Ref: 7
Topic: Communication as transaction

38) Rhetoric is another term for communication that focuses on individual efforts to use words and symbols to achieve their goals.

Answer: TRUE
Page Ref: 7
Topic: The rich heritage of public speaking

39) Diverse audiences have different expectations for appropriate and effective topics, structure, language, and delivery.

Answer: TRUE
Page Ref: 10
Topic: Public speaking & diversity

40) Adapting to diverse audiences shows that speakers are audience-centered in delivering their information.

Answer: TRUE
Page Ref: 10
Topic: Public speaking & diversity

41) It is unrealistic to try to eliminate speech anxiety because almost everyone experiences some degree of anxiety when speaking.

Answer: TRUE
Page Ref: 11
Topic: Understand your nervousness

42) Visualizing yourself giving the entire speech as a controlled, confident speaker will limit your anxiety.

Answer: TRUE
Page Ref: 15
Topic: Develop & deliver organized speech, visualize your success

43) What does it mean to be "empowered" in public speaking?

Page Ref: 2
Topic: Why study public speaking? empowerment

44) Explain how a source and a receiver operate in a public speaking setting.

Page Ref: 6
Topic: Communication as action, source & receiver

45) Discuss how diverse audiences have an impact on planning and preparing a speech.

Page Ref: 10-11
Topic: Public speaking & diversity

46) Described in the textbook were four styles of communication apprehension: average style, insensitive style, inflexible style, and confrontation style. Briefly describe each one.

Page Ref: 12
Topic: Understand your nervousness

47) Discuss the rich heritage of public speaking beginning with the Greeks to the present. Give specific examples of the differences in presentation style for each era.
Page Ref: 7-9
Topic: The rich heritage of public speaking

48) List and explain the similarities and differences between public speaking and conversation.
Page Ref: 3-5
Topic: Public speaking & conversation

49) There are five factors in the "communication as action" process, according to your text. List them and offer a brief definition or explanation of each term.
Page Ref: 5-6
Topic: The communication process, communication as action

50) In this chapter the authors offered a number of ideas on how to develop and deliver a well-organized speech. List and explain at least 5 of these ideas, showing how each can help in reducing speaker anxiety.
Page Ref: 14-18
Topic: Develop and deliver a well-organized speech

Chapter 2 The Audience-Centered
Speechmaking Process

1) Being an audience-centered public speaker
   A) is an option to consider for some speeches.
   B) sometimes influences the topics you choose.
   C) influences every step of the speech making process.
   D) does not require that the culture of the audience be considered.

   Answer: C
   Page Ref: 25
   Topic: Consider your audience
   Skill: Definition Question

2) When selecting and narrowing a speech topic, speakers need to consider
   A) the audience, occasion, and themselves.
   B) the support material, audience , and time limits.
   C) the occasion, the purpose, and content.
   D) the audience, purpose, and occasion.

   Answer: A
   Page Ref: 26
   Topic: Select and narrow your topic
   Skill: Definition Question

3) The three types of general speech purposes are
   A) to entertain, to inform, and to persuade.
   B) to entertain, to introduce, and to inform.
   C) to persuade, to convince, and to move to action.
   D) to inform, to demonstrate, and to persuade.

   Answer: A
   Page Ref: 27
   Topic: Determine your purpose
   Skill: Definition Question

4) A speech that reinforces attitudes, beliefs, values, or behaviors is
   A) a persuasive speech purpose.   B) an informative speech purpose.
   C) an explanatory speech purpose.   D) a demonstration speech purpose.

   Answer: A
   Page Ref: 27
   Topic: Determine your purpose
   Skill: Definition Question

5) What aspect of speech preparation contains the one-sentence summary or the essence of your message?

    A) the general-purpose statement   B) the central idea

    C) the specific-purpose statement   D) the supporting material

Answer: B
Page Ref: 29
Topic: Develop your central idea
Skill: Definition Question

6) The ability to develop or discover ideas that result in new insights or new approaches to old problems is referred to as

    A) creativity.   B) retooling.   C) invention.   D) inventory.

Answer: C
Page Ref: 29
Topic: Generate the main ideas
Skill: Definition Question

7) The three major divisions of a speech are

    A) the introduction, the preview, and the main points.

    B) the introduction, the body, and transitions.

    C) the introduction, the body, and the conclusion.

    D) the introduction, the conclusion, and the delivery.

Answer: C
Page Ref: 32
Topic: Organize your speech
Skill: Definition Question

8) The purpose of an introduction is

    A) to move your audience to action.

    B) to get the audience's attention and provide an overview.

    C) to summarize the key ideas.

    D) to tell what all of your sources are.

Answer: B
Page Ref: 32
Topic: Organize your speech
Skill: Definition Question

9) When preparing a presentation, speakers should focus on the central element of

    A) the topic.   B) the occasion.

    C) the audience.   D) the speaker themselves.

Answer: C
Page Ref: 25
Topic: Consider your audience
Skill: Description Question

10) From topic selection to outlining, what should be the central focus in speech preparation?

    A) delivery   B) the occasion   C) the speaker   D) the audience

Answer: D
Page Ref: 25
Topic: Consider your audience
Skill: Description Question

11) To which type of general speech purpose do the terms defining, clarifying, illustrating, and elaborating refer?

    A) to inform   B) to entertain   C) to persuade   D) to inspire

Answer: A
Page Ref: 27
Topic: Determine your purpose
Skill: Description Question

12) The specific purpose of speeches

    A) is to inform, persuade, or entertain.

    B) is what the speaker wants the audience to remember, do, or feel after the speech.

    C) is a one-sentence summary of the whole speech.

    D) is the essence of the speech message.

Answer: B
Page Ref: 27
Topic: Determine your purpose
Skill: Description Question

13) When choosing supporting materials for a topic,

    A) use a variety of materials that appeal to the senses.

    B) trust yourself as an authority and just use your own knowledge.

    C) use as many facts and statistics as possible to prove you have done your research.

    D) go to the Internet and use mainly these sources to assure a current, fresh topic.

Answer: A
Page Ref: 30
Topic: Gather verbal and visual supporting material
Skill: Description Question

14) The process of relating abstract concepts or statistics to something concrete

    A) will confuse and frustrate the audience.

    B) is time consuming for the speaker; a distraction for the audience.

    C) will help communicate the ideas more clearly to the audience.

    D) may over simplify the content and turn off the audience from listening.

Answer: C
Page Ref: 30
Topic: Gather verbal and visual supporting material
Skill: Description Question

15) A thorough outline of your speech is necessary

    A) to be certain that every word of your speech is written out.

    B) so that your teacher has something to follow during your speech.

    C) to ensure a definite, logical organization of the material you have gathered.

    D) so you will have something to speak from during your presentation.

Answer: C
Page Ref: 32
Topic: Organize your speech
Skill: Description Question

16) What does your textbook say is the best way to rehearse a speech?

    A) alone, in a room in which you are most comfortable

    B) in your head rather than aloud, to maximize your spontaneity when you give the speech

    C) aloud, standing just as you will when you deliver the speech to your audience

    D) aloud, but seated and with your eyes closed so as to reduce anxiety

Answer: C
Page Ref: 34
Topic: Rehearse your speech
Skill: Description Question

17) Looking over her speech, Wendi was pleased with her topic, how well the speech was outlined and organized, and the number of sources she had to share. Should these items be the central focus of this speech?

    A) Yes; it is important to have a strong, organized message.

    B) Yes; without a number of sources for support, the message will only be considered her opinion.

    C) No; without the addition of visual aids, she won't be able to convey a clear meaning.

    D) No; in public speaking the central focus should be the listeners.

Answer: D
Page Ref: 25
Topic: Consider your audience
Skill: Example Question

18) How should a speaker select and narrow a topic?

    A) by considering the audience

    B) by considering the occasion

    C) by considering their own interests, talents, and experiences

    D) all of the above

Answer: D
Page Ref: 26–27
Topic: Select and narrow your topic
Skill: Example Question

19) In a speech about voting trends, Michael cited recent statistics, but made no attempt to appeal to the audience's sense of patriotism or to encourage them to vote more regularly. What is Michael's general purpose in this speech?

    A) to persuade   B) to entertain   C) to inform   D) to motivate

Answer: C
Page Ref: 27
Topic: Determine your purpose
Skill: Example Question

20) At the beginning of his outline, Ambrose wrote, "At the end of my speech, the audience will be able to describe the steps necessary in changing a flat tire." This statement is an example of

    A) a general purpose.   B) a specific purpose.
    C) a central idea.   D) a main idea.

Answer: B
Page Ref: 27–28
Topic: Determine your purpose
Skill: Example Question

21) In her speech about giving blood, Krysten challenges her audience to sign up and give blood at next week's blood drive on campus. The purpose of her speech was to

    A) inspire.   B) persuade.   C) inform.   D) entertain.

Answer: B
Page Ref: 27
Topic: Determine your purpose
Skill: Example Question

22) In your speech about American government, you simply subdivide your central idea into the three branches of government. According to the text, how are you subdividing your central idea in this speech?

    A) showing several reasons why your central idea is true

    B) supporting your central idea with a series of steps

    C) using a "development over time" system of dividing points

    D) finding logical divisions in your central idea

Answer: D
Page Ref: 29
Topic: Generate the main ideas
Skill: Example Question

23) Travis presented a speech that consisted of a long list of statistics on auto sales in America. What technique should he have used to clarify and add interest to these statistics?

   A) Put the statistics on an overhead transparency.

   B) Repeat the statistics at least twice.

   C) Make each statistics a main idea of the speech.

   D) Compare the statistics to something the audience knows.

   Answer: D
   Page Ref: 30
   Topic: Gather verbal and visual supporting material
   Skill: Example Question

24) How should speakers practice before giving a speech?

   A) Speakers should read the speech several times to themselves in order to memorize the content.

   B) Speaker should concentrate on the movement and gestures to be used because the speech is already written.

   C) Speakers should present the information out loud, as they would in front of an audience.

   D) Speakers should practice many times so they use the exact same words every time.

   Answer: C
   Page Ref: 34–35
   Topic: Rehearse your speech
   Skill: Example Question

25) Jane was working on her informative speech for speech class. In college, she is a declared business major with interests in finance and accounting. As a result, she came up with the idea of telling her audience about the technical aspects of tax accounting--her passion. Will this be a good topic for her speech class?

   A) Yes; Jane has the enthusiasm to present the topic to the class.

   B) Yes; Jane has a great deal of research and technical information for support.

   C) No; Jane may have a passion for the topic, but she hasn't considered her audience.

   D) No; Jane does not have the expertise to present this information to the audience.

   Answer: C
   Page Ref: 25
   Topic: Consider your audience
   Skill: Application Question

26) Yolanda was looking forward to giving her informative speech because she liked her topic—her hometown. However, when she gave the speech, the audience seemed disinterested; she couldn't understand why she got such negative audience feedback. Given this information about the situation, what was Yolanda's mistake?

   A) She violated several ethical principles of public speaking.

   B) She didn't have enough research and statistics in the speech to make it interesting.

   C) She confused the roles of speaker and listener.

   D) She was speaker-centered rather than audience-centered in her topic selection.

   Answer: D
   Page Ref: 25
   Topic: Consider your audience
   Skill: Application Question

27) Steven gave an informative speech on scuba diving. He brought in the equipment, showed how to use the gear, talked about dive records, how to go about taking lessons, where the best diving was, and the dangers of diving. Although it was initially interesting, the speech became too technical, the audience lost interest, and Steven went over his time limit by four minutes. Based on this, what was Steven's mistake?

   A) poor topic selection   B) lack of organization
   C) failing to narrow the topic   D) not enough support information

   Answer: C
   Page Ref: 26
   Topic: Select and narrow your topic
   Skill: Application Question

28) Lateshiya was planning a dental hygiene speech for the third graders at Thompson Elementary. She would be telling them how to brush and care for their teeth in a ten to fifteen minute speech. This is a topic she is very comfortable with because she is the dental assistant to Dr. Smith, the local dentist. In order to select the appropriate topic for the time allowed, Lateshiya should consider

   A) the introduction, body, and conclusion.

   B) the general purpose, specific purpose, and central idea.

   C) the audience, the occasion, and the speaker.

   D) the visual, mediated, and verbal supporting materials.

   Answer: C
   Page Ref: 26
   Topic: Select and narrow your topic
   Skill: Application Question

29) Sam presented an informative speech on hurricanes. He described the origins of earthquakes, how they develop, which areas of the earth are prone to hurricanes, how hurricanes are rated, the damage they do, and what to do when one hits. The speech was dry and the audience was bored. From this description, what was Sam's mistake?

A) poor topic selection

B) lack of appropriate research

C) incoherent organization

D) failing to narrow his topic

Answer: D
Page Ref: 26–27
Topic: Select and narrow your topic
Skill: Application Question

30) In her introduction, Monique makes the statement, "If you learn the Heimlich maneuver in my speech today, it is possible that you could save the life of your mother, your father, or your best friend." You recognize this statement as

A) a central idea.

B) a conclusion

C) a specific-purpose statement.

D) a preview statement.

Answer: C
Page Ref: 30
Topic: Develop your central idea
Skill: Application Question

31) Shantal had a speech to prepare. She selected a topic, did her research, and sat down to draft the speech. She wrote out the introduction first, then wrote a version of the intro that she would use as a conclusion. Then she outlined the main points of the body of the speech. Is this a "textbook" way to organize a speech?

A) Yes; your text says to draft an introduction first, since it's the first thing you'll say in the speech; then draft the body, then the conclusion.

B) No; your text suggests to start with the body of the speech first, then go back and draft the intro.

C) Yes; your text does not suggest any particular order for drafting the three sections of a speech.

D) No; your text suggests to draft the conclusion first, then the intro, then the body, because conclusions usually don't get enough attention if you work on them last.

Answer: B
Page Ref: 32
Topic: Organize your speech
Skill: Application Question

32) Jason had thoroughly researched his speech on the art of tattooing. He had many different types of supporting material; the speech was well organized. He was certain that this was a great speech. In the library, right before the speech, he printed out his complete outline. When presenting his speech to the class, he had to read from his outline and became nervous and anxious. Which of the following statements best pertains to this situation?

A) Jason forgot to visualize success, which would have helped reduce his nervousness.

B) Jason's mistake was that he didn't have enough good supporting material.

C) Jason procrastinated and didn't have time to rehearse his speech aloud and on his feet.

D) Jason forgot to organize his speech in a way that made sense to his audience.

Answer: C
Page Ref: 34
Topic: Rehearse your speech
Skill: Application Question

33) The needs, attitudes, beliefs, values, and other characteristics of the speaker should play a leading role in every step of the speech making activity.

Answer: FALSE
Page Ref: 25
Topic: Consider your audience

34) Being audience–centered is a continual, ongoing process within speech making.

Answer: TRUE
Page Ref: 25
Topic: Consider your audience

35) The physical surroundings, as well as the occasion, have minimal impact on the formality the audience expects in the choice of topics.

Answer: FALSE
Page Ref: 26
Topic: Select and narrow your topic

36) The three types of general purposes for giving a speech are to inform, to persuade, and to entertain.

Answer: TRUE
Page Ref: 27–28
Topic: Determine your purpose

37) A specific–purpose statement is a statement of your major ideas.

Answer: FALSE
Page Ref: 27–28
Topic: Determine your purpose

38) The central idea is a one-sentence summary of the main ideas in a speech.

Answer: TRUE
Page Ref: 29
Topic: Develop your central idea

39) Intention is the ability to develop and discover ideas that result in new insights or new approaches to old problems.

Answer: TRUE
Page Ref: 29
Topic: Generate the main ideas

40) Concrete supporting material is more interesting to most people than abstract ideas.

Answer: TRUE
Page Ref: 30
Topic: Gather verbal and visual supporting material

41) Introductions and conclusions should be prepared before you have organized the body of your speech.

Answer: FALSE
Page Ref: 32
Topic: Organize your speech

42) Memorize your speech so you won't forget any of the words.

Answer: FALSE
Page Ref: 34
Topic: Rehearse your speech

43) Why should public speaking be an audience-centered activity, rather than a speaker-centered activity? Provide two reasons.
Page Ref: 25-26
Topic: Consider your audience

44) What is the most effective way to word a specific purpose statement?
Page Ref: 27-28
Topic: Determine your purpose

45) What is the most effective way to develop your main ideas?
Page Ref: 27-29
Topic: Determine purpose and develop central idea

46) In what ways can verbal and visual supporting material enhance a presentation?
Page Ref: 30-31
Topic: Gather verbal and visual supporting material

47) Delivery is the final stage of the speech making process. What does the speaker need to consider at this stage?

Page Ref: 36
Topic: Deliver your speech

48) You have been given the assignment of writing an informative speech for this class. Choose a topic based on your personal interests or experience and explain how you could develop that topic and relate it to your audience.

Page Ref: 25-26
Topic: Consider your audience

49) Chapter 2 has focused on the speech making process. In any speech, there are three major organizational divisions. List and explain each division. What must the speaker focus on in each area?

Page Ref: 32-34
Topic: Organize your speech

50) Your speech topic is "How to Build a Birdhouse." In a rather well developed essay, discuss what the speaker needs to consider when developing this idea into a speech.

Page Ref: 27-36
Topic: purpose, main ideas, gather material, organize & rehearse

Chapter 3   Ethics and Free Speech

1) Our beliefs, values, and moral principles by which we determine what is right or wrong are our

    A) laws.   B) ethics.   C) truths.   D) rules.

Answer: B
Page Ref: 42
Topic: Ethics
Skill: Definition Question

2) According to the National Communication Association, this is fundamental to responsible thinking, decision making, and the development of relationships and communities within and across contexts, cultures, channels, and media. This is

    A) free speech.   B) truth.

    C) ethnocentric communication.   D) ethical communication.

Answer: D
Page Ref: 42
Topic: Ethics
Skill: Definition Question

3) This type of speech or speech act is legally protected

    A) ethical speech.   B) critical speech.

    C) free speech.   D) political speech.

Answer: C
Page Ref: 42
Topic: Free speech
Skill: Definition Question

4) The U. S. Constitution states, "Congress shall make no law...abridging the freedom of speech." This is part of the

    A) First Amendment.   B) Fourth Amendment.

    C) Fifth Amendment.   D) Tenth Amendment.

Answer: A
Page Ref: 43
Topic: Speaking freely
Skill: Definition Question

5) Lifting key passages from sources you do not credit in your speech is an unethical practice known as

    A) paraphrasing.   B) misquoting.   C) attribution.   D) plagiarism.

Answer: D
Page Ref: 47
Topic: Speaking ethically, avoid plagiarism
Skill: Definition Question

6) When citing your sources orally in a speech, you should

    A) say "quote, unquote."   B) make quote signs with your fingers.

    C) state briefly the author, title, year.   D) give the full Internet address.

Answer: C
Page Ref: 48
Topic: Speaking ethically, acknowledge sources
Skill: Definition Question

7) As ethical listeners, audience members must

    A) expect a coherent, organized, complete presentation.

    B) gain the speakers main points, even if there is no outside support or evidence.

    C) watch and listen, but don't focus on verbal or nonverbal feedback.

    D) formulate questions based on information that wasn't clearly supported or stated.

Answer: A
Page Ref: 51
Topic: Listening ethically, communicate expectations and feedback
Skill: Definition Question

8) Critical listening means that you, as a listener,

    A) are courteous and tolerant of the speaker.

    B) attempt to learn and retain the information presented.

    C) hold the speaker to his or her ethical responsibilities.

    D) remember the main ideas and organization presented.

Answer: C
Page Ref: 52
Topic: Listening ethically, listen critically
Skill: Definition Question

9) What must balance the right to free speech?

    A) the responsibility of speaking effectively

    B) the responsibility of speaking ethically

    C) the responsibility of citing sources of information

    D) the responsibility of addressing diversity

Answer: B
Page Ref: 42
Topic: Ethics
Skill: Description Question

10) In 1989, the Supreme Court overturned a statute that made burning the United States flag illegal because

    A) they found it to be a "speech act" protected by the First Amendment.

    B) they believed pornography was a more important issue to consider.

    C) they were persuaded by the Berkeley Free Speech movement.

    D) there were not enough cases to warrant a Consitutional amendment.

Answer: A
Page Ref: 43
Topic: Speaking freely
Skill: Description Question

11) One month after September 11, 2001, the Patriot Act was put into place to

    A) give each person the opportunity to speak freely with limited restrictions.

    B) broaden the investigative powers of government agencies in matters of national security.

    C) limit the function of the American Civil Liberties Union.

    D) bring to light the unethical motives of free speech.

Answer: B
Page Ref: 44
Topic: Speaking freely
Skill: Description Question

12) When speakers consider beliefs, values, and moral principles when writing and presenting a speech, they are

    A) speaking freely.   B) speaking ethically.

    C) speaking to the needs of the audience   D) speaking to persuade the audience.

Answer: B
Page Ref: 45
Topic: Speaking ethically
Skill: Description Question

13) In the 1950's, Senator Joseph McCarthy convinced the American public that Communists were infiltrating every aspect of their lives by

    A) providing strong evidence and reasoning.

    B) honestly and ethically trying to save the country.

    C) substantiating his claims with specific examples.

    D) distorting the truth and manipulating emotions.

Answer: D
Page Ref: 45
Topic: Speaking ethically, use sound evidence and reasoning
Skill: Description Question

14) Hypothetical illustrations within a speech are
   A) acceptable especially when other evidence can't be found to support the speech.
   B) acceptable to show what might happen, as long as the speaker is clear that it is hypothetical.
   C) unacceptable because they are unethical and deceptive.
   D) unacceptable to bring into a speech, especially if solid, current evidence is available.

Answer: B
Page Ref: 46-47
Topic: Speaking ethically, be honest
Skill: Description Question

15) With regard for those "gray areas" of ethics pertaining to the use of sources in a speech, your text suggests
   A) when in doubt, document all of your sources in a speech.
   B) when in doubt, omit sources from your speech.
   C) when in doubt, include sources in a written bibliography, but don't cite them orally.
   D) when in doubt, use common knowledge rather than published sources.

Answer: A
Page Ref: 48-51
Topic: Speaking ethically, acknowledge sources
Skill: Description Question

16) If you disagree with a speaker's ideas and dislike his or her delivery, you should
   A) dismiss the speaker, simply because you differ in preferences for speaking styles.
   B) frown and shake your head at the speaker to communication your displeasure.
   C) tactfully communicate verbally, in a question-and-answer session, your disagreement.
   D) realize this speaker is not worth listening to, and just tune out.

Answer: C
Page Ref: 51
Topic: Listening ethically, communicate expectations and feedback
Skill: Description Question

17) When a person decides not to overestimate or falsify an insurance claim just to have the extra money, this action is based on the individuals
   A) own cultural norms.   B) objective rules.
   C) fairness code.   D) code of ethics.

Answer: D
Page Ref: 42
Topic: Ethics
Skill: Example Question

18) If you attempt to convince listeners that they should find small ways to "get back at the government" by cheating on their income tax returns, you are violating a speaking ethic which expects speakers to

    A) use sound evidence and reasoning.   B) have a clear, responsible goal.

    C) acknowledge their sources.   D) give the listener choices.

Answer: B
Page Ref: 45
Topic: Speaking ethically, have a clear, responsible goal
Skill: Example Question

19) Speakers who bring in false claims and tug at the emotions of the audience, instead of using sound evidence and logical arguments, are examples of

    A) untrustworthy speakers.   B) unimaginative speakers.

    C) uneffective speakers.   D) unethical speakers.

Answer: D
Page Ref: 45
Topic: Speaking ethically, use sound evidence and reasoning
Skill: Example Question

20) In a persuasive speech, you tell a hypothetical story in your introduction and represent it as actually happening to you. Is this appropriate?

    A) Yes, because it will have strong emotional appeal which will sway your audience.

    B) Yes, because your overall goal of the speech is clear and responsible.

    C) No, because only factual stories should be used as introductory devices.

    D) No, because you are violating an ethical principle which requires that speakers be honest.

Answer: D
Page Ref: 46–47
Topic: Speaking ethically, be honest
Skill: Example Question

21) For a persuasive speech, you find a couple books in the Library and several Internet sources that support your position perfectly. You copy this information and weave these ideas and pieces of evidence into the speech that you give to the class. Is this ethical?

    A) Yes; you have done your own work and have written your own speech.

    B) Yes; all this information was found in open–access areas.

    C) No; this speech is an example of patchwork plagiarism which is unethical.

    D) No; Internet sources have questionable credibility thus making the speech unethical.

Answer: B
Page Ref: 47
Topic: Speaking ethically, avoid plagiarism
Skill: Example Question

22) Ralph found an excellent source for his speech on organic gardening. He brought the author's scientific evidence on earthworms and ladybugs into his speech outline. Is this ethical?

   A) No; this is unethical because it is patchwork plagiarism.

   B) No; this is unethical because Ralph is not an expert in organic gardening.

   C) Yes; this is ethical as long as Ralph gives credit to the author in a bibliography.

   D) Yes; this is ethical as long as Ralph cites his source orally within the speech.

Answer: D
Page Ref: 47
Topic: Speaking ethically, avoid plagiarism
Skill: Example Question

23) When the speaker began, Georgia looked up, smiled, and made eye contact with the speaker. Her behavior is called

   A) listening critically.   B) showing your sensitivity to differences.

   C) communicating your expectations.   D) exercising your own freedom of speech

Answer: C
Page Ref: 51
Topic: Listening ethically, communicate expectations and feedback
Skill: Example Question

24) While listening to a classmate's speech, Sean began to think that the speaker was citing sources that were biased. Sean began to shake his head and frown. What was Sean doing in this instance?

   A) communicating his expectations as a listener to the speaker

   B) attempting to be tolerant of differences between himself and the speaker

   C) providing inappropriate nonverbal feedback to the speaker

   D) listening critically and giving feedback to the speaker

Answer: D
Page Ref: 52
Topic: Listening ethically, listen critically
Skill: Example Question

25) Eric wanted to use an excerpt from a *Nightline* episode, as both an audiovisual aid and a source for his speech. But he only agreed with and wanted to use one of the two guests' interaction with Ted Koppell, so he edited out the second guest and showed the edited videotape. Was this ethical?

   A) Yes; this kind of "sound biting" goes on all the time and is completely ethical.

   B) No; this kind of "sound biting" violates the ethical guideline of using sound evidence and reasoning.

   C) Yes; this technique is ethical because the speaker has the audience's best interests at heart.

   D) No; by editing the show, Eric is plagiarizing *Nightline*—a serious ethical violation.

Answer: B
Page Ref: 42
Topic: Ethics
Skill: Application Question

26) Tee gave an informative speech on the poor drinking water conditions of local water. He brought in a test kit and presented statistics that proved local water was dangerous to drink. He advised the class to purchase a certain type of water filter pitcher guaranteed to remove these impurities. At the end of his speech, he mentioned that he worked for the company that made the pitcher and had them for sale. What was Tee's mistake?

   A) Tee used too much evidence and reasoning for an informative speech.

   B) Tee's speech was actually illegal, in that he was advertising in class.

   C) Tee used coercion when suggesting that the audience buy the product from him.

   D) Tee violated the ethical guideline of having a responsible goal for a speech.

   Answer: D
   Page Ref: 45
   Topic: Speaking ethically, have a clear, responsible goal
   Skill: Application Question

27) While researching, Gabe found a tragic story about a young girl who died from a drunk driving accident. In presenting his speech, Gabe told the story as if this girl was his sister. The speech was quite moving and afterward everyone told Gabe how sorry they were for his family. At this time, he told them it wasn't really his sister but thought that telling it that way was more effective for this speech. Why is this unethical?

   A) Gabe violated an ethical principle that requires speakers to avoid plagiarism.

   B) Gabe violated an ethical principle that requires speakers to be tolerant of differences.

   C) Gabe violated an ethical principle that requires speakers not to misrepresent information.

   D) Gabe violated an ethical principle that requires speakers to do their own work.

   Answer: C
   Page Ref: 46–47
   Topic: Speaking ethically, be honest
   Skill: Application Question

28) Marty is having problems coming up with an idea for a speech. He knows his fraternity keeps files of old tests, papers, and speeches and decides to look through these for an idea. He finds a great speech about bats, their value to ecology, and their habitat. He likes this speech so much that he decides to use it largely intact but goes to the Internet to update the sources. Which of the following statements best describes this situation?

   A) This is an ethical violation known as plagiarism.

   B) This is a violation of individuals' freedom of speech.

   C) This is not plagiarism because the fraternity's files are general knowledge.

   D) This is not plagiarism; it's an example of good time management.

   Answer: A
   Page Ref: 47
   Topic: Speaking ethically, avoid plagiarism
   Skill: Application Question

29) Mindy and Karla are roommates; both are taking public speaking, but from different instructors. In preparation for an upcoming class speech, they decide to do the same topic, work together in the library to gather the research, and draft an outline. After all, two heads are better than one, right? They then each deliver the speech in their respective speech classes. Which of the following statements best pertains in this situation?

    A) This is not an ethical violation as long as each speaker makes the speech a little bit different in the actual delivery.

    B) It is not an ethical violation to use the same outline, but they shouldn't use exactly the same sources in the speech.

    C) This is an ethical violation known as plagiarism, because the two roommates did not do their own original work in preparing the speech.

    D) This is not the best example of ethical behavior, but it's not a serious ethical violation because they are in separate classes with different instructors.

Answer: C
Page Ref: 48
Topic: Speaking ethically, do your own work
Skill: Application Question

30) Maggie has decided on an informative speech on the topic of dreaming. She finds three different articles that cover areas that she believes will be of interest to her audience. Although she credits these sources in her written citation page, she imports intact the ideas and support from these sources as her speech's main ideas and supporting material. Which of the following statements best pertains to this situation?

    A) There is no ethical violation here, as she has credited these sources on the outline.

    B) There is no ethical violation here, as long as the ideas work well together.

    C) There is an ethical violation here known as patchwork plagiarism.

    D) There is an ethical violation here, as speakers must have more than three sources.

Answer: C
Page Ref: 47-48
Topic: Speaking ethically, avoid plagiarism
Skill: Application Question

31) In a speech on breast cancer, you decide to use the latest information from the National Breast Cancer Foundation website, www.nationalbreastcancer.org. What is the proper way to cite this source in your speech?

    A) "According to www.nationalbreastcancer.org..."

    B) "According to National Breast Cancer Foundation researchers, in their October 2004 article titled, 'NBCF Supports M. D. Anderson Cancer Center's Breakthrough Cancer Research', found at www.nationalbreastcancer.org..."

    C) "The National Breast Cancer Foundation in 2004 stated..."

    D) These sources should only be cited in the bibliography, not during the speech.

Answer: C
Page Ref: 48
Topic: Speaking ethically, acknowledge sources
Skill: Application Question

32) When Aaron gave his speech on capital punishment, he noticed quizzical, confused looks on audience members' faces when he offered statistics about capital punishment as a deterrent to crime. Is there any ethical violation in this example?

   A) No; listeners were behaving ethically by communicating nonverbally their feedback to the speaker.
   B) No; listeners are usually confused when a topic that is controversial is presented by a speaker.
   C) Yes; listeners have an ethical responsibility to only smile and nod in approval to a speaker.
   D) Yes; listeners were unethical in being selfish and expressing their disagreement with the speaker.

   Answer: A
   Page Ref: 51
   Topic: Listening ethically, communicate expectations and feedback
   Skill: Application Question

33) Ethics are the beliefs, values, and moral principles by which people determine what is right or wrong.

   Answer: TRUE
   Page Ref: 42
   Topic: Ethics

34) Ethical communication implies honesty and respect for oneself and others.

   Answer: TRUE
   Page Ref: 42
   Topic: Ethics

35) Ethics are universal; all cultures hold the same basic, human ethics.

   Answer: FALSE
   Page Ref: 42
   Topic: Ethics

36) The First Amendment to the Constitution guarantees our freedom of speech.

   Answer: TRUE
   Page Ref: 43
   Topic: Speaking freely

37) The American Civil Liberties Union was founded in 1964, at the University of California in Berkeley, which changed the political climate of U. S. college campuses.

   Answer: FALSE
   Page Ref: 43
   Topic: Speaking freely

38) Accommodation means that speakers should not abandon their own convictions in order to show tolerance of the audience's beliefs.

Answer: TRUE
Page Ref: 46
Topic: Speaking ethically, sensitive to and tolerant of difference

39) Using someone else's outline to help you prepare a speech assignment is a form of plagiarism.

Answer: TRUE
Page Ref: 48
Topic: Speaking ethically, do your own work

40) Speakers have an ethical responsibility to give credit for information and ideas that are not their own.

Answer: TRUE
Page Ref: 48
Topic: Speaking ethically, acknowledge sources

41) When quoting someone's words in a presentation, you should always say, "Quote....unquote" to indicate where the idea begins and ends.

Answer: FALSE
Page Ref: 48–49
Topic: Speaking ethically, acknowledge sources

42) Courtesy and tolerance are the same as approval and agreement.

Answer: FALSE
Page Ref: 52
Topic: Listening ethically, listen critically

43) Define free speech and ethics and their impact on public speaking.
Page Ref: 42
Topic: Ethics

44) What does it mean to "have a clear, responsible goal" in public speaking? Give an example for support.
Page Ref: 45
Topic: Speaking ethically, have a clear, responsible goal

45) What is patchwork plagiarism as related to public speaking? Provide a few examples.
Page Ref: 47
Topic: Speaking ethically, avoid plagiarism, your own work

46) What steps can a speaker take in order to avoid plagiarism? Give an example for support.
Page Ref: 47–51
Topic: Speaking ethically, avoid plagiarism

47) How is critical listening different from normal, everyday listening and thinking?

Page Ref: 52
Topic: Listening ethically, listen critically

48) Discuss the history of free speech in the United States beginning with the Constitution in 1791 until the present. Give specific examples for each era discussed.

Page Ref: 43–44
Topic: Speaking freely and ethically

49) Discuss the ethical consequences of lying or exaggerating about the information you present to your audience. Use recent events as examples to support your position.

Page Ref: 45–51
Topic: Speaking ethically

50) According to the authors, what four types of supporting material must be orally cited in a speech? How is citing information orally in a speech different from citing information in writing?

Page Ref: 48
Topic: Speaking ethically, acknowledge sources

Chapter 4 Listening to Speeches

1) Because we hear so many sounds simultaneously, the first stage of listening is to

    A) attend.   B) select.   C) understand.   D) remember.

Answer: B
Page Ref: 58
Topic: Barriers to effective listening, selecting
Skill: Definition Question

2) When we, as listeners, focus on the the message, we are said to

    A) attend.   B) understand.   C) select.   D) remember.

Answer: A
Page Ref: 58
Topic: Barriers to effective listening, attending
Skill: Definition Question

3) When listeners assign meaning and make sense of what they heard, they have _____ the message

    A) selected   B) attended   C) understood   D) remembered

Answer: C
Page Ref: 59
Topic: Barriers to effective listening, understanding
Skill: Definition Question

4) When listeners can recall ideas and information presented to them, they are said to

    A) attend.   B) select.   C) remember.   D) understand.

Answer: C
Page Ref: 59
Topic: Barriers to effective listening, remembering
Skill: Definition Question

5) Because much of our day is spent listening, there may be times we "tune out" when information is being sent to us. This process is called

    A) psychological noise.   B) information fatigue.

    C) psychological distractions.   D) information overload.

Answer: D
Page Ref: 59
Topic: Barriers to effective listening, information overload
Skill: Definition Question

6) When you decide that the speaker's message will have no value, even before the speech begins, you have engaged in the listening barrier of

    A) information overload.   B) personal concerns.

    C) jumping to conclusions.   D) prejudice.

Answer: D
Page Ref: 60
Topic: Barriers to effective listening, prejudice
Skill: Definition Question

7) Listeners who may be uncomfortable or nervous about new information, or fear they may misunderstand or misinterpret the information, are said to have

    A) receiver apprehension.   B) information overload.

    C) listener distraction.   D) receiver concern

Answer: A
Page Ref: 61
Topic: Barriers to effective listening, receiver apprehension
Skill: Definition Question

8) As audience members, if we prefer to listen to complex information that is interspersed with facts and details, we are

    A) people-oriented listeners.   B) action-oriented listeners.

    C) content-oriented listeners.   D) time-oriented listeners.

Answer: C
Page Ref: 66
Topic: Understand your listening style
Skill: Definition Question

9) Listeners who are able to evaluate the reasoning, logic, and quality of the speaker's message are engaged in

    A) critical thinking.   B) effective listening.

    C) inference evaluation.   D) fact gathering.

Answer: A
Page Ref: 70
Topic: Listening and critical thinking
Skill: Definition Question

10) When, as a listener, you relate what you hear to an experience that you had as a teenager, you are

    A) attending.   B) selecting.   C) understanding.   D) remembering.

Answer: C
Page Ref: 59
Topic: Barriers to effective listening, understanding
Skill: Description Question

11) What type of listening style occurs when you want the speaker to get to the point and state what needs to be done?

    A) people-oriented style.   B) action-oriented style.

    C) content-oriented style.   D) time-oriented style.

Answer: B
Page Ref: 66
Topic: Understand your listening style
Skill: Description Question

12) While listening to a sociology lecture, you mentally rearrange the ideas being presented, summarize the information, and remain alert for key information. You are considered

    A) an average listener.   B) an active listener.

    C) an ethical listener.   D) an entertained listener

Answer: B
Page Ref: 67
Topic: Become an active listener
Skill: Description Question

13) Evaluating the quality of information, ideas, and arguments presented by a speaker is

    A) critical listening   B) critical thinking.

    C) fact finding.   D) inference evaluation.

Answer: A
Page Ref: 70
Topic: Listening and critical thinking
Skill: Description Question

14) As listeners, if we become aware of the methods and techniques speakers use to achieve their goals while speaking, what are we listening for?

    A) the symbols that are brought into the speech

    B) the rhetorical strategies employed by the speakers

    C) the rhetorical criticism used within the presentation

    D) the inferences or facts presented during the speech

Answer: B
Page Ref: 74-75
Topic: Identifying and analyzing rhetorical strategies
Skill: Description Question

15) To achieve their speaking goals, speaker will employ methods and techniques known as

    A) rhetorical listening   B) rhetorical criticism

    C) rhetorical strategies   D) rhetorical symbolism

Answer: C
Page Ref: 74
Topic: Identifying and analyzing rhetorical strategies
Skill: Description Question

16) If the speech teacher asked the class to "judge or discuss" the speeches given in class, what would the teacher want from the class?

A) The class would be asked to give "criticism" or constructive feedback to the speaker.

B) The class would talk about what they heard in the speeches that day.

C) The class would be asked to give "thumbs up" or "thumbs down".

D) The class would offer rhetorical strategies for future speakers.

Answer: A
Page Ref: 76
Topic: Giving feedback to others
Skill: Description Question

17) When Jenny heard the speech about the sinking of the Titanic presented in her class, she thought the speech was on the movie of the same name. What was Jenny's problem?

A) listening, but not understanding   B) listening, but not remembering

C) listening, but not organizing   D) listening, but not evaluating

Answer: A
Page Ref: 58-59
Topic: Barriers to effective listening
Skill: Example Question

18) In her class speech about traditions on her college campus, Angela provides little known facts that she discovered in her research. Is this a good technique, according to your text?

A) No, because this information is too mundane for the audience to be concerned about.

B) Yes, but only if the little known facts are humorous, because humor is what really keeps an audience's attention.

C) No; in a class speech you should refrain from too much detail or you will lose the attention of your audience.

D) Yes; using new or little known information is an effective listening technique that helps keep the audience's attention.

Answer: D
Page Ref: 59
Topic: Barriers to effective listening
Skill: Example Question

19) Joseph is easily distracted from a speech by noise outside the classroom, worries about his girlfriend, and then decides that the speech is boring, anyway. How would your text classify Joseph?

A) He is an empathetic listener.   B) He is a poor listener.

C) He is a selfish listener.   D) He is a critical listener.

Answer: B
Page Ref: 59
Topic: Barriers to effective listening
Skill: Example Question

20) You've been to four classes in one day. In each class, you've listened to a lecture and taken notes. By the time you get to your night class, you feel like you just can't take in another word. What is the textbook term for what you're experiencing?

    A) lack of academic discipline   B) attention deficit disorder

    C) information overload   D) information prejudice

    Answer: C
    Page Ref: 59
    Topic: Barriers to effective listening, information overload
    Skill: Example Question

21) If you're worried that your speech to the PTA on the need for more parental volunteerism will cause the audience to lose attention, what should you do, according to your textbook chapter on listening?

    A) You should build in redundancy and make your ideas really clear, so as to avoid the speech rate-thought rate difference.

    B) You should make the speech as short as possible, while still managing to include your main points.

    C) You should probably not do a speech at all if you think the audience will lose attention; instead, simply do a discussion or question-and-answer session.

    D) There is really nothing a speaker can do in a situation like this; if the audience loses attention, that is their fault and they should have stayed at home.

    Answer: A
    Page Ref: 61
    Topic: Differences between speech rate and thought rate
    Skill: Example Question

22) In her speech about the black granite Vietnam war memorial and what it represents, Charlotte becomes a bit emotional, her voice choking up a little. This causes Jan, an audience member, to become emotional too. What type of listening is occurring in this situation?

    A) listening for pleasure   B) listening to empathize

    C) listening to evaluate   D) listening for information

    Answer: B
    Page Ref: 64–65
    Topic: Becoming a better listener, identify listening goal
    Skill: Example Question

23) When Zelda begins her speech, Conner thinks to himself, "Oh no; every time she says she's going to take 10 minutes we're in here for 30 minutes. I wish she would just get to her point and not be so long-winded so I can get my job done!" What listening style is Conner exhibiting?

    A) He is a people-oriented listener.   B) He is an action-oriented listener.

    C) He is a content-oriented listener.   D) He is a time-oriented listener.

    Answer: D
    Page Ref: 66
    Topic: Understand your listening style
    Skill: Example Question

24) After listening to a speech by a local politician, Jon had the opportunity to think about the speech. He discovered that evidence was misquoted, there were a number of scare tactics used, and some data was made up to support the points being made. What did Jon discover?

A) If the speech was understandable to the audience, then the politician could use any means available to present the information to the audience.

B) Not all audiences need current and relevant data to make up their minds.

C) He discovered that the politician used unethical rhetorical strategies to manipulate the audience.

D) The politician focused on making sure he had an effective and appropriate message.

Answer: C
Page Ref: 74
Topic: Identifying and analyzing rhetorical strategies
Skill: Example Question

25) Jan has had a full week at school. She's turned in two research papers and studied for a mid-term. Because she wants to remember the material presented and she realizes the importance of being a good listener, Jan

A) focuses on the visual aids.   B) focuses on the examples.

C) focuses on the main ideas.   D) focuses on the speaker.

Answer: C
Page Ref: 64
Topic: Becoming a better listener, listen for major ideas
Skill: Application Question

26) Tara comes into the classroom early on the day of her speech. She closes the blinds, checks the room temperature, and sets up the transparency machine. Which barrier to listening is Tara trying to overcome?

A) information overload   B) personal concerns

C) outside distractions   D) receiver apprehension

Answer: C
Page Ref: 60
Topic: Barriers to effective listening, outside distractions
Skill: Application Question

27) Jeb is really very intelligent, but when he gives speeches he tends to go monotone, he mumbles a lot, and he doesn't move around much or use many gestures. Most listeners have trouble tuning in to Jeb, even though his speech content is often excellent. Which tip to increase your listening efficiency offered in your text best applies in this instance?

   A) Listen with your eyes as well as your ears, because nonverbals speak volumes.

   B) Avoid outside distractions that may interfere with your ability to listen effectively.

   C) Avoid jumping to conclusions even if you disagree with the speaker's points.

   D) Adapt to the speaker's delivery by focusing on the message, not the delivery style.

Answer: D
Page Ref: 63
Topic: Becoming a better listener, adapt to speaker's delivery
Skill: Application Question

28) In a speech about how Texas became a state, Martina provided three main points and delivered them in a chronological pattern. Two of her classmates, Anna and Donna, were discussing the speech the next day. Anna remembered Martina's three main points while Donna only remembered the story used in the introduction. Who was the better listener, according to the textbook's tips to enhance listening skills?

   A) Anna was the better listener because she followed the tip, "Listen for major ideas."

   B) Donna was the better listener because she followed the tip, "Be a selfish listener."

   C) Anna was the better listener because she followed the tip, "Avoid overreacting emotionally."

   D) Donna was the better listener because she followed the tip, "Avoid information overload."

Answer: A
Page Ref: 64
Topic: Becoming a better listener, listen for major ideas
Skill: Application Question

29) Peter is listening to a speech on stem cell research. He's trying to take down everything the speaker is saying because it seems that everything is important. Is this considered good listening, according to your text?

   A) Not really, because it is better to just listen to a speech than to take any notes.

   B) Yes, because he is actively involved in listening to the speech.

   C) Yes, because he is writing down everything said, rather than merely the key ideas.

   D) Not really, because taking down everything said can cause a listener to miss key ideas.

Answer: D
Page Ref: 69
Topic: Improving your note-taking skill
Skill: Application Question

30) When Kalia quoted Samuel Jones in supporting her opposition to the war in Afghanistan, John became concerned. What aspect of critical listening had alerted John?

   A) John did not know if Jones was an expert source as Kalia had not qualified him.

   B) John did not believe that the war in Afghanistan was a topic worth discussing.

   C) John believed that Kalia should have had some statistics before citing Jones.

   D) John believed that the quality of the evidence presented was not valid

   Answer: A
   Page Ref: 70
   Topic: Listening and critical thinking
   Skill: Application Question

31) Robin listened to Rick's speech on interesting sights for tourists in San Francisco. She analyzed Rick's effectiveness as a speaker and evaluated the speech as a success. Which three criteria did Robin use, as suggested by your text, for the evaluation and analysis of a speech?

   A) The message should be clearly organized, persuasive, and have a smooth delivery.

   B) The message should be understood by the audience, achieve its purpose, and be ethical.

   C) The message should be reasonable in purpose, well researched, and logical in organization.

   D) The message should be useful to the audience, informative, and easily understood.

   Answer: B
   Page Ref: 72
   Topic: Analyzing and evaluating speeches
   Skill: Application Question

32) Krysten just listened to Erin's speech about the Lord of the Rings Trilogy. In her written critique, Krysten made the following comments: "I liked the visuals," "Weak eye contact," and "The conclusion was good." According to the text, is this a good critique?

   A) No; Krysten should have provided more descriptive information to Erin to reflect the specific strengths and weaknesses of the speech

   B) No; Krysten did not talk about the introduction and body of the speech.

   C) Yes; Krysten put into writing what she thought was good and what needed work.

   D) Yes; Krysten provided sufficient feedback so Erin can make corrections in future speeches.

   Answer: A
   Page Ref: 76–78
   Topic: Giving feedback to others
   Skill: Example Question

33) Active listening involves selecting, attending, understanding, and remembering.

   Answer: TRUE
   Page Ref: 58
   Topic: Barriers to effective listening

34) We listen at a much slower rate than the rate an average person speaks.

Answer: FALSE
Page Ref: 60
Topic: Barriers to effective listening, prejudice

35) When you make a quick decision as to whether or not to accept a speaker's idea, it increases your ability as a listener.

Answer: FALSE
Page Ref: 61
Topic: Differences between speech rate and thought rate

36) Heightened emotions will assist our ability in understanding the speaker's message.

Answer: FALSE
Page Ref: 63
Topic: Monitor your emotional reaction to a message

37) Listening skills do not develop automatically, they are developed through practice.

Answer: TRUE
Page Ref: 66
Topic: Practice listening

38) Knowing your listening style can help you become a better and more flexible listener.

Answer: TRUE
Page Ref: 66
Topic: Understand your listening style

39) Critical thinking is a mental process of making judgments about the conclusions presented by what you see, hear, and read.

Answer: TRUE
Page Ref: 70
Topic: Listening and critical thinking

40) There is little difference between a fact and an inference.

Answer: FALSE
Page Ref: 70
Topic: Listening and critical thinking

41) A speaker has applied rhetorical criticism if he or she offers appropriate evidence to reach a valid, well-reasoned conclusion.

Answer: FALSE
Page Ref: 71
Topic: Evaluate the underlying logic and reasoning

42) Detecting faulty reasoning in a speech means that you're listening effectively because you're thinking critically.

Answer: TRUE
Page Ref: 71
Topic: Evaluate the underlying logic and reasoning

43) Describe and give an example of the four stages of good listening.
Page Ref: 58-59
Topic: Barriers to effective listening

44) What is "receiver apprehension"? What steps can one take to overcome this listening problem?
Page Ref: 61-62
Topic: Barriers to effective listening, receiver apprehension

45) What is the difference between "active listening" and "critical listening"? Briefly discuss how each applies to public speaking.
Page Ref: 67
Topic: Becoming a better listener, become an active listener

46) List and briefly explain the four listening styles presented in the text.
Page Ref: 66
Topic: Understand your listening style

47) Discuss at length what skills are necessary in order to be an effective critical listener.
Page Ref: 70-72
Topic: Listening and critical thinking

48) According to your text, six barriers may interfere with your ability to listen effectively. In a well-developed, thorough essay, explain each barrier and provide an example of how each applies to the public speaking context.
Page Ref: 58-62
Topic: Barriers to effective listening

49) There are nine ways that a person can improve her or his listening ability. In a well-developed essay, select four of these methods. Explain what each means and offer an example of how each applies to a public speaking situation.
Page Ref: 62-68
Topic: Becoming a better listener

50) Your textbook provides several suggestions for analyzing and evaluating speeches, as well as for evaluating your own performances. In an in-depth essay, first discuss the important role that feedback and evaluation play in the development of one's speaking skills. Then discuss two of the guidelines for evaluating others' presentations and two for evaluating your own speaking abilities.
Page Ref: 72-79
Topic: Analyzing and evaluating speeches

Chapter 5   Analyzing Your Audience

1) A speaker who analyses the listeners and the occasion and adapts the speech to them is defined by your text as

    A) a hard-working speaker.   B) an audience-centered speaker.

    C) an over-zealous speaker.   D) a goal-centered speaker.

Answer: B
Page Ref: 84
Topic: Becoming an audience-centered speaker
Skill: Definition Question

2) Information such as age, race, gender, education, and religious views are part of

    A) ethnicity.   B) demographics.

    C) speech content.   D) socioeconomic status.

Answer: B
Page Ref: 85
Topic: Gather information about your audience, demographics
Skill: Definition Question

3) To gather formal information about audience members' attitudes, beliefs, and values, you can

    A) observe them before you speak.

    B) engage them in conversation prior to the speech.

    C) research the group you're speaking to on the internet or in other publications.

    D) ask open-ended and closed-ended questions on a survey.

Answer: D
Page Ref: 86
Topic: Gather information about your audience
Skill: Definition Question

4) To establish common ground with your audience members, you should

    A) acknowledge the differences but not change the speech content.

    B) focus on the differences to establish the outline of your speech.

    C) try to maximize similarities and minimize differences between you and the audience.

    D) maximize similarities and maximize the differences for a good balance of information.

Answer: C
Page Ref: 88
Topic: Analyze information about your audience, common ground
Skill: Definition Question

5) What is ethnocentrism?

   A) the belief that almost everyone in a cultural group will agree on core belief and values

   B) the attitude that the diverse cultural beliefs around the world should be respected by all

   C) the belief that although cultures are different, they all favor peace and harmony

   D) the attitude that one's own cultural approach is superior to those from other cultures

Answer: D
Page Ref: 91
Topic: Demographic audience analysis; culture, ethnicity, and race
Skill: Definition Question

6) As defined by your text, analyzing the audience's income, occupation, and education refers to

   A) ethnicity.   B) cultural identifiers.

   C) socioeconomic status.   D) individualism.

Answer: C
Page Ref: 94
Topic: Analyze your audience before you speak, socioeconomic status
Skill: Definition Question

7) A segment of your audience that you most want to address or influence is the

   A) target audience.   B) intended audience.

   C) diverse audience.   D) influential audience.

Answer: A
Page Ref: 95
Topic: Adapting to diverse listeners, focus on a target audience
Skill: Definition Question

8) Trying to determine what an audience believes or thinks about a speech topic is termed

   A) psychological analysis.   B) demographic analysis.

   C) informational analysis.   D) environmental analysis.

Answer: A
Page Ref: 97–98
Topic: Psychological audience analysis
Skill: Definition Question

9) All of the following are ways to customize your message to your audience EXCEPT

   A) talking about the town, city, or community of the audience members.

   B) presenting significant events that happened on the date you are speaking.

   C) referring to your most recent accomplishments in your career.

   D) referring to recent news events.

Answer: C
Page Ref: 108
Topic: Strategies for customizing your message to your audience
Skill: Definition Question

10) In discovering that the audience members have similar cultural characteristics, are about the same age, and have relatively the same education level--although they don't have the same socioeconomic background--the speaker is trying to discover

    A) audience beliefs.
                        B) common ground.

    C) values.
                              D) audience feelings.

Answer: B
Page Ref: 88
Topic: Analyze information about your audience, common ground
Skill: Description Question

11) Collecting information about an audience concerning their age range, gender, and ethnicity is part of

    A) a situational analysis.
                        B) a demographic analysis.

    C) a diversity analysis.
                        D) a psychological analysis.

Answer: B
Page Ref: 90
Topic: Analyzing your audience, demographic audience analysis
Skill: Description Question

12) That portion of a person's background that relates to a national or religious heritage is known as

    A) cultural identity.
                        B) ethnicity.

    C) race.
                              D) an audience analysis.

Answer: B
Page Ref: 91
Topic: Demographic audience analysis; culture, ethnicity, and race
Skill: Description Question

13) The specific group of audience members that you, as a speaker, most wish to address or influence is your

    A) uninterested audience.
                      B) target audience.

    C) diverse audience.
                        D) captive audience.

Answer: B
Page Ref: 95
Topic: Adapting to diverse listeners, focus on a target audience
Skill: Description Question

14) The textbook recommends this, whether separately or with a target audience focus, when reflecting the diversity of your audience:

    A) focusing on one important element to bring the audience together

    B) using repetition patterns to reiterate your point

    C) speaking as though the audience is universal

    D) using a variety of strategies to reach the different listeners

Answer: D
Page Ref: 95–96
Topic: Diverse listeners, diverse strategies for a diverse audience
Skill: Description Question

15) Which of the following concepts in a psychological analysis are the audience's concepts of right and wrong, good and bad?

    A) beliefs   B) values   C) attitudes   D) feelings

Answer: B
Page Ref: 98
Topic: Psychological audience analysis
Skill: Description Question

16) A situational audience analysis includes an evaluation of

    A) the attitude, beliefs, and the values that are held by your audience.

    B) the age, gender, ethnicity, race, and culture of your audience.

    C) the time and place of your speech, the size of your audience, and the occasion.

    D) the influence of your audience based on income, occupation, and education.

Answer: C
Page Ref: 100
Topic: Situational audience analysis
Skill: Description Question

17) Finding out that your speech will be given to a all-male audience around the age of 30 is a form of

    A) situational analysis.   B) psychological analysis.

    C) demographic analysis.   D) socioeconomic analysis.

Answer: C
Page Ref: 90
Topic: Demographic audience analysis
Skill: Example Question

18) When a speaker uses terms like "African-American" and "Asian-American" the speaker is

    A) attending to cultural elements of psychological audience analysis.

    B) attending to elements of situational audience analysis.

    C) attending to ethnic elements of demographic audience analysis.

    D) attending to racial elements of psychological audience analysis.

Answer: C
Page Ref: 91
Topic: Demographic audience analysis; culture, ethnicity, and race
Skill: Example Question

19) Audience members who place more importance on nonverbal than verbal messages from a speaker might be from _____ cultures, whereas those placing more emphasis on what was said than the nonverbal messages might be from _____ cultures.

    A) low context; high context   B) low power; high power

    C) individualistic; collectivistic   D) high context; low context

Answer: D
Page Ref: 91-92
Topic: Demographic audience analysis; culture, ethnicity, and race
Skill: Example Question

20) It is important to know the approximate education level of your audience because

    A) people with more education usually have more income.

    B) people with more education usually have a larger vocabulary.

    C) people with more education usually expect more from a speaker.

    D) people with more education usually work harder than other people.

Answer: B
Page Ref: 94
Topic: Analyze your audience before you speak, socioeconomic status
Skill: Example Question

21) In your speech on gays in the military, you make a reference to "those homosexuals." As an audience-centered speaker, what error did you make?

    A) You did not relate the speech to everyone in the audience.

    B) You were not sensitive in the use of your language to diversity.

    C) You did not analyze the audience to check their attitude on this subject.

    D) You made the mistake of not caring who you offended in your speech.

Answer: B
Page Ref: 91
Topic: Analyzing your audience before you speak, sexual orientation
Skill: Example Question

22) As a requirement for your biology class, you must attend a speech by a visiting scholar in biology. What kind of audience will you be a member of at this event?

A) a captive audience

B) a voluntary audience

C) a demographic audience

D) all of the above

Answer: A
Page Ref: 99
Topic: Psychological audience analysis, speech class as audience
Skill: Example Question

23) A good speaker should ethically use the information gathered in an audience analysis so that the message will be clearly understood by them. According to your text, this process is called

A) audience reception.

B) audience adaptation.

C) audience knowledge.

D) audience attention.

Answer: B
Page Ref: 89
Topic: Adapt to your audience
Skill: Example Question

24) You're deciding on a speech topic, but need some information from your audience. Rather than asking them to divulge out loud their opinions on a couple of topics, you design a short questionnaire. The questionnaire asks whether a person agrees or disagrees with a series of statements regarding various topics. What form of survey are you using?

A) an open-ended, formal audience analysis survey

B) a close-ended, informal audience analysis survey

C) a close-ended, formal audience analysis survey

D) an open-ended, informal audience analysis survey

Answer: C
Page Ref: 86
Topic: Gather information about your audience
Skill: Application Question

25) For his informative speech assignment, Greg has chosen the World Bank as his topic. But before he develops this speech any further, he compiles a questionnaire for the audience to determine their personal knowledge, interest, and attitudes about this issue. What is the term for this technique?

A) formal audience analysis

B) informal audience analysis

C) formal situational analysis

D) informal situational analysis

Answer: A
Page Ref: 85-86
Topic: Gather information about your audience
Skill: Application Question

26) As part of planning for her class speech on the Patriot Act, Brenda passed around a brief questionnaire asking whether her classmates were for or against the Act, did they think parts or all of the Act should change, etc. Was this a good idea, according to your text?

    A) No; by doing the questionnaire, she revealed to the class what her speech topic was going to be.

    B) Yes; this is a smart technique of analyzing the audience known as demographic audience analysis.

    C) No; the class is a captive audience, so finding out their views ahead of time wasn't necessary.

    D) Yes; this is a form of psychological audience analysis—a good thing to do for any kind of audience.

Answer: D
Page Ref: 97–98
Topic: Psychological audience analysis
Skill: Application Question

27) Brent was presenting a speech on childhood diabetes, a disease that he had suffered from for years. He decided not to mention this fact to his audience. According to your text, which statement concerning Brent's speech is more correct?

    A) A speaker's personal experience makes him more credible to his audience.

    B) A speaker needs only facts and figures to build his credibility to the audience.

    C) A speaker should not mention personal experiences, as they sound like bragging.

    D) A speaker should not mention personal experiences, as they sound self-pitying.

Answer: A
Page Ref: 100
Topic: Analyzing attitudes toward you, the speaker
Skill: Application Question

28) You think you want to do your persuasive speech on capital punishment, taking the stance that capital punishment is a deterrent to crime and just punishment. But before you craft this speech, you would like to learn your audience's views on the subject. What should you do?

    A) Conduct an analysis to reveal your audience's beliefs on the subject.

    B) Conduct an analysis to reveal your audience's attitudes on the subject.

    C) Conduct an analysis to reveal your audience's values underlying their beliefs.

    D) none of the above

Answer: B
Page Ref: 98
Topic: Psychological audience analysis
Skill: Application Question

29) Savena needed room to move during her speech, but when she arrived to make her presentation, she learned that she would have to use a microphone affixed to a lectern. What was Savena's mistake?

   A) not conducting a pre-speech audience analysis

   B) not conducting a pre-speech formal demographic analysis

   C) not conducting a pre-speech situational analysis

   D) not conducting a pre-speech informal psychological analysis

Answer: C
Page Ref: 101
Topic: Situational audience analysis
Skill: Application Question

30) When Robert asked his class, "How many of you just don't have enough time to do all the things you want to do in a day?" as his speech introductory device, almost everyone in the audience raised their hands. Robert took this audience reaction as

   A) an indication of verbal responsiveness.

   B) inappropriate crossing of the lines between speaker and listener.

   C) restless movement, which indicated to Robert that he'd better get on with his speech.

   D) an indication of nonverbal responsiveness.

Answer: D
Page Ref: 105
Topic: Identifying nonverbal audience cues
Skill: Example Question

31) TJ is giving a speech on reasons why recycling is everyone's responsibility. During this speech, TJ notices that his audience isn't making eye contact with him, that there is a lot of restless movement, and that the audience's faces seem blank. How should TJ respond to this negative feedback?

   A) Speak slower so the audience understands.

   B) Ignore the audience and stay with his notes.

   C) Clarify the point with some significant statistics.

   D) Illustrate the point with a funny, personal example.

Answer: D
Page Ref: 105–106
Topic: Identifying nonverbal cues, responding to nonverbal cues
Skill: Application Question

32) Veronica was watching her audience carefully during her speech. After a few minutes, she noticed several class members staring at her with a glazed look in their eyes. She immediately picked up the speed of her speech and moved on to a colorful visual. What was Veronica responding to?

    A) psychological audience cues   B) situational feedback

    C) nonverbal audience cues   D) listener anxiety

Answer: C
Page Ref: 105–106
Topic: Identifying nonverbal cues, responding to nonverbal cues
Skill: Application Question

33) When considering your audience, consider them as a group, rather than individuals.

Answer: FALSE
Page Ref: 84
Topic: Becoming an audience-centered speaker

34) Before preparing a speech, it is helpful to analyze the audience demographically, psychologically, and situationally.

Answer: TRUE
Page Ref: 90
Topic: Analyze your audience before you speak

35) Closed–ended questions are used when a speaker wants specific information from an audience.

Answer: TRUE
Page Ref: 86
Topic: Gather information about your audience

36) If a speech is well written, it can be presented to anyone, anytime.

Answer: FALSE
Page Ref: 84–85
Topic: Becoming an audience-centered speaker

37) According to your text, to establish common ground with your audience you should maximize the differences and minimize the similarities.

Answer: FALSE
Page Ref: 88
Topic: Analyze information about your audience, common ground

38) Ethnocentrism is the same thing as patriotism.

Answer: FALSE
Page Ref: 91
Topic: Demographic audience analysis; culture, ethnicity, and race

39) Australia, Canada, Great Britain, Belgium, Denmark and the United States are considered collectivistic cultures because they place greater emphasis on individual achievement, encourage personal accomplishment, and look out for individual achievements

Answer: FALSE
Page Ref: 92
Topic: Individualistic and collectivistic cultures

40) Knowing what religious group, political group, work group, or social group an audience member identifies with will help the speaker make inferences about the listeners likes, dislikes, beliefs, and values.

Answer: TRUE
Page Ref: 93
Topic: Group membership

41) Audience diversity only involves the factors of ethnic and cultural differences.

Answer: FALSE
Page Ref: 90–94
Topic: Analyze your audience before you speak

42) Nonverbal responses at the end of the speech may express some general feeling of the audience, but they are not much help in identifying which strategies were the most effective.

Answer: TRUE
Page Ref: 105–106
Topic: Identifying nonverbal cues, responding to nonverbal cues

43) What are the three steps needed to help us become an audience-centered speaker? Briefly explain each.
Page Ref: 84–96
Topic: Becoming an audience-centered speaker

44) You have been asked to speak to a sorority pledge class on your campus. In a brief essay, describe the demographic audience analysis you would conduct on this audience.
Page Ref: 90–97
Topic: Analyze your audience before you speak

45) Briefly explain the differences between demographic audience analysis and a psychological audience analysis.
Page Ref: 90–100
Topic: Analyze your audience before you speak

46) What is a target audience? What does the speaker need to consider when addressing a target audience?
Page Ref: 95
Topic: Adapting to diverse listeners, focus on a target audience

47) What are three reasons to conduct a situational analysis prior to giving a speech?

Page Ref: 100–103
Topic: Situational audience analysis

48) Imagine that you have been asked to speak to a Sunday morning church school class comprised mainly of elderly church members. Using the key elements of audience analysis, provide a thorough, demographic audience analysis and psychological audience analysis of this group.

Page Ref: 90–100
Topic: Analyze your audience before you speak

49) For your speech class, you know the speech topic you have chosen could be considered highly controversial. Using a hypothetical topic, develop a questionnaire to find out as much as possible about your audience's attitudes, beliefs, and values concerning this topic. Use both open–ended and close–ended questions.

Page Ref: 85–87
Topic: Gather information about your audience

50) Even though the audience for your speech is a voluntary one, you suspect that they will likely be uninterested in your topic and unfavorable to the proposals you will make in your speech. Using a hypothetical situation and speech topic, describe what strategies you might use to hold their attention and persuade them to accept your proposals.

Page Ref: 94–97
Topic: Adapting to diverse listeners

Chapter 6 Developing Your Speech

1) Craig prepared a speech on the women's movement and presented it in his women's studies class. His speech was inappropriate because, while he spoke on a topic of interest, he did not take into account:

   A) that the audience was both male and female.

   B) that the audience members were not alive during this event.

   C) that he was speaking on something only he was interested in.

   D) the knowledge the audience already had about the subject.

   Answer: D
   Page Ref: 117
   Topic: Select and narrow your topic, guidelines for selecting topic
   Skill: Application Question

2) Federica is the editor of the school newspaper. She prepares a speech about the future of the paper and intends to deliver it at the next staff meeting. Federica is appealing to her audience by:

   A) presenting a speech of little interest but in a humorous way.

   B) choosing a speech topic that matters to her listeners as well as to herself.

   C) demonstrating that she has done her research about the newspaper's future.

   D) giving a speech outside of her public speaking class.

   Answer: B
   Page Ref: 117
   Topic: Select and narrow your topic, guidelines for selecting topic
   Skill: Application Question

3) When selecting a topic for a speech, speakers needs to consider the audience, the occasion, and

   A) the length of time needed for the speech.

   B) the setting where the speech will be given.

   C) the speakers themselves.

   D) the knowledge of the audience regarding the topic.

   Answer: C
   Page Ref: 117–119
   Topic: Select and narrow your topic, guidelines for selecting topic
   Skill: Definition Question

4) Speeches that you present will be either to inform, to persuade, or to entertain. This goal for your speech is knows as its

   A) general purpose.   B) specific purpose.

   C) central idea.   D) blueprint.

   Answer: A
   Page Ref: 123
   Topic: Determine your purpose, general purpose
   Skill: Definition Question

5) This statement is decided solely by the speaker since it depends on the behavioral change the speaker expects from the audience at the end of the speech.

   A) general purpose.   B) specific purpose.

   C) central idea.   D) functional purpose.

   Answer: B
   Page Ref: 124
   Topic: Determine your purpose, specific purpose
   Skill: Definition Question

6) A complete declarative sentence that summarizes your speech is known as the

   A) general purpose.   B) specific purpose.

   C) central idea.   D) blueprint.

   Answer: C
   Page Ref: 127
   Topic: Develop your central idea
   Skill: Definition Question

7) Searching for logical divisions in a subject is a strategy for

   A) determining your general purpose.   B) determining your specific purpose.

   C) determining your preview statement.   D) determining your main ideas.

   Answer: D
   Page Ref: 131
   Topic: Generate and preview your main idea, generating main ideas
   Skill: Definition Question

8) According to your text, a combination of your central idea and a summary of your main points is known as the

   A) general purpose.   B) specific purpose.

   C) central idea.   D) blueprint.

   Answer: D
   Page Ref: 133
   Topic: Previewing your main ideas, blueprint
   Skill: Definition Question

9) When you discover the listener's needs, interests, and expectations prior to selecting a topic, you are fulfilling which guideline for selecting a topic?

    A) Consider yourself.   B) Consider the occasion.

    C) Consider the audience.   D) Consider the topic.

Answer: C
Page Ref: 117
Topic: Select and narrow your topic, guidelines for selecting topic
Skill: Description Question

10) Is it appropriate to develop a speech topic based on something you heard on a television talk show?

    A) No; using televised information for your speech topic is a form of plagiarism.

    B) No; most topics discussed on talk shows are inappropriate speech material.

    C) Yes, but you have to address the topic the same way the talk show did.

    D) Yes; brainstorming ideas from a television program is a good way to develop a topic and is an option suggested in the text.

Answer: D
Page Ref: 119–120
Topic: Strategies for selecting a topic
Skill: Description Question

11) When you make a list of your own interests, and just begin writing as many topics related to these as you can think of without stopping to consider them, you are using a technique known as

    A) topic building.   B) brainstorming.

    C) natural topic selection.   D) webbing.

Answer: B
Page Ref: 119
Topic: Strategies for selecting a topic
Skill: Description Question

12) When searching for a speech topic, Web directories, such as Yahoo, are helpful because

    A) they have a list of topics divided into categories and subcategories.

    B) the present material in many different ways.

    C) the information provided in Web directories is always accurate.

    D) Web directories will have better ideas for topics than you will.

Answer: A
Page Ref: 121
Topic: Narrowing the topic
Skill: Description Question

13) When starting with a broad speech topic such as "automobiles," it is necessary to narrow it down because

    A) not everyone in the class is interested in the topic of automobiles.

    B) there is too much research involved in such a broad topic.

    C) you can't cover everything about automobiles in a speech.

    D) your speech would probably be too long and boring.

Answer: B
Page Ref: 122
Topic: Narrowing the topic
Skill: Description Question

14) During your speech you ask your audience to sign a petition increasing the student parking areas. Your general goal is:

    A) to inform.   B) to notify.   C) to entertain.   D) to persuade.

Answer: D
Page Ref: 124
Topic: Determine your purpose, general purpose
Skill: Description Question

15) A complete central idea or thesis statement should be all of the following EXCEPT

    A) a complete declarative sentence.

    B) a sentence with direct, specific language.

    C) a statement with at least three ideas.

    D) an audience-centered idea.

Answer: C
Page Ref: 127
Topic: Develop your central idea
Skill: Description Question

16) When you structure your speech topic into main points, based on a reasonable, appropriate progression of ideas, what aspect of organization are you accomplishing?

    A) developing a clear central idea   B) narrowing the topic

    C) generating supporting material   D) finding logical divisions

Answer: D
Page Ref: 131
Topic: Generate and preview main ideas, finding logical divisions
Skill: Description Question

17) Emily has been asked to speak to a group of her colleagues at work about a new project, but she wonders, "What do these people already know about this project, and are they excited about it?" These questions reflect Emily's

    A) lack of self-esteem as a public speaker.

    B) consideration for the occasion for which she's speaking.

    C) concern about the interests and knowledge of her audience.

    D) lack of sophistication in audience analysis techniques.

Answer: C
Page Ref: 117
Topic: Select and narrow your topic, guidelines for selecting topic
Skill: Example Question

18) For his graduation ceremony, when Brady decided to give his valedictory address on the topic of opposition to the rising costs of university tuition, Brady failed to

    A) consider the occasion.   B) narrow his topic.

    C) conduct a demographic analysis.   D) consider the audience.

Answer: A
Page Ref: 118
Topic: Guidelines for selecting a topic, consider the occasion
Skill: Example Question

19) An informative speech has been assigned, so Angel starts to worry about what he can possibly present to his class. That night he takes out a blank sheet of paper and just starts writing down every possible idea for a speech topic that he can think of. What is Angel doing?

    A) topic narrowing   B) brainstorming

    C) procrastinating   D) searching

Answer: B
Page Ref: 119
Topic: Strategies for selecting a topic
Skill: Example Question

20) It's the end of the semester, your brain is fried, and you just can't come up with a creative topic for your persuasive speech. As a last resort, you pick up the daily newspaper and decide on a topic by looking at one of the headlines. According to your textbook, is this advisable?

    A) No; it is a form of plagiarism when you get speech topics from a newspaper.

    B) No; newspapers offer boring material which do not make for a good topic.

    C) Yes, but topics generated from newspapers take much longer to develop than others.

    D) Yes; scanning newspaper headlines may be an effective strategy to find a speech topic.

Answer: D
Page Ref: 120
Topic: Selecting a topic, listening and reading for topic ideas
Skill: Example Question

21) "At the end of my speech, my audience will understand the three different types of Reggae music," is an example of

    A) a central idea.   B) a general purpose.

    C) a specific purpose.   D) a blueprint.

Answer: C
Page Ref: 125
Topic: Specific purpose, formulating the specific purpose
Skill: Example Question

22) The central idea for your speech on "Use sunscreen" just will not break itself down into logical divisions. Rather than forget this topic and try to find one that divides more logically, what does your text suggest you do?

    A) Find a chronological pattern for the main ideas.

    B) Establish reasons why your central idea is true.

    C) Don't worry about it, the audience won't notice anyway.

    D) Find new supporting material on the topic and start again.

Answer: B
Page Ref: 131–132
Topic: Generate and preview your main ideas, establishing reasons
Skill: Example Question

23) "I'm going to talk about the sport of racquetball, including the history of the game, some of the basic equipment used when playing racquetball, and some of the health benefits derived from the sport." An audience member would recognize this as

    A) an attention-getter.   B) a blueprint statement.

    C) a specific purpose.   D) a general purpose.

Answer: B
Page Ref: 133
Topic: Previewing your main ideas, blueprint
Skill: Example Question

24) If a speaker says, "Tonight, I'm going to discuss with you two reasons why everyone should recycle, including cost-saving benefits and the problems waste creates in the environment," you recognize this as

    A) a general purpose statement.   B) an attention-getting device.

    C) a preview of main ideas.   D) a specific purpose statement.

Answer: C
Page Ref: 133
Topic: Previewing your main ideas
Skill: Example Question

25) Marilee was preparing for her persuasive speech assignment. However, she couldn't come up with a good topic. After scanning a few magazines, the newspaper, and the Web for an idea, Marilee still hasn't found a good topic. When she did think of something she immediately dismissed it thinking, "That topic stinks; the class would be bored!" What technique should Marilee utilize in this situation?

   A) piggybacking   B) brainstorming
   C) audience analysis   D) logical divisions

Answer: B
Page Ref: 119
Topic: Strategies for selecting a topic, brainstorming
Skill: Application Question

26) You have been assigned a 5-7 minute informative speech and have chosen the topic of film directing. You have plenty of sources and clear main ideas. However, in your presentation of the speech, you run way over time. What is the problem in this instance?

   A) a poor sense of organization and logical division of information

   B) a failure to consider your audience when researching

   C) a failure to appropriately narrow your speech topic

   D) a failure to construct a behavioral objective.

Answer: C
Page Ref: 122
Topic: Narrowing the topic
Skill: Application Question

27) Anne–Marie spoke to the local Chamber of Commerce, attempting to influence the members to work together to generate a more hospitable city for tourists. However, the members expected Anne–Marie merely to tell them her findings on the city's progress in the last two years. Which of the following statements best pertains to this situation?

   A) Anne–Marie's problem was in her general speech purpose; she persuaded when she should have informed the audience.

   B) Anne–Marie's problem was in her specific speech purpose; she informed when she should have simply entertained the audience.

   C) Anne–Marie's problem was in failing to narrow down her speech topic so that the speech would be appropriate for her audience.

   D) Anne–Marie's problem was in audience analysis; she failed to analyze the demographics of her audience prior to the speech.

Answer: A
Page Ref: 123–124
Topic: General purpose, speaking to inform, to persuade
Skill: Application Question

28) When Elizabeth was asked to be the after-dinner speaker for the senior honors dinner, she responded with great enthusiasm. She viewed this as an opportunity to reflect on their past years at college as well as bring a smile to her fellow seniors' faces, to make them feel the excitement of the event, and to help them enjoy themselves. In this situation, Elizabeth would be

A) speaking to inform.   B) speaking to persuade.

C) speaking to convince.   D) speaking to entertain.

Answer: D
Page Ref: 124
Topic: General purpose, speaking to entertain
Skill: Application Question

29) In a speech about the importance of establishing a daily exercise routine, Bart sums up his goal for the speech in the following statement: "At the end of my speech, the audience will be inspired to initiate a daily exercise routine." You recognize this statement as

A) a general purpose statement.   B) a specific purpose statement.

C) a concluding statement.   D) a summary statement.

Answer: B
Page Ref: 124
Topic: Determine your purpose, specific purpose
Skill: Application Question

30) On Barnett's speech outline appeared the sentence: "Censorship of the music industry violates our First Amendment right to free speech." You recognize this statement as

A) a general purpose statement.   B) a specific purpose statement.

C) a central idea or thesis.   D) an inflammatory statement.

Answer: C
Page Ref: 127
Topic: Develop your central idea
Skill: Application Question

31) Allison has written and rewritten the central idea of her speech on "Dog Care." She finally comes up with " Dog care is very difficult ." What is the problem with this central idea?

A) Her central idea is not audience-centered.

B) Her central idea is too confusing.

C) Her central idea is too vague.

D) Her central idea is not a declarative sentence.

Answer: C
Page Ref: 128
Topic: Develop your central idea
Skill: Application Question

32) Derrick's speech on rodeos focused on three different events. His central ideas was "The modern rodeo has many interesting events including bronco busting, calf roping, and bull riding." Derrick's central idea could be readily broken down into main ideas based on

    A) a chronological order or series of steps.   B) reasons to show the central idea is true.

    C) logical division of the central idea.   D) the relative importance of each idea.

Answer: C
Page Ref: 131
Topic: Generate and preview main ideas, finding logical divisions
Skill: Application Question

33) In a speech that is under ten minutes in length, you should allow at least one week from topic selection to speech delivery.

Answer: TRUE
Page Ref: 116
Topic: Developing your speech

34) In business, when giving a presentation for your company, the topic is usually chosen and defined for you.

Answer: TRUE
Page Ref: 117
Topic: Select and narrow your topic

35) To be successful, a topic should be appropriate for the audience, not necessarily focusing on the occasion.

Answer: FALSE
Page Ref: 118
Topic: Consider the occasion

36) Brainstorming is a method of finding topic ideas by carefully considering each idea.

Answer: FALSE
Page Ref: 119
Topic: Strategies for selecting a topic

37) It's a poor idea to watch TV, read books, or scan through magazines in search of a speech topic, because using one of these topics is a form of plagiarism.

Answer: FALSE
Page Ref: 119-121
Topic: Strategies for selecting a topic

38) Once the topic of the speech is found the speaker needs to narrow the topic, but the speaker doesn't need to consider the time limit of the speech assignment until speech day.

Answer: FALSE
Page Ref: 122-123
Topic: Narrowing the topic

39) With a general purpose of "to inform," a speaker offers information to change or reinforce an audience's convictions.

Answer: FALSE
Page Ref: 123
Topic: General purpose, speaking to inform

40) The specific purpose, unlike the general purpose, is decided by you alone because it depends directly on the topic you choose.

Answer: TRUE
Page Ref: 124
Topic: Determine your purpose, specific purpose

41) A central idea can be worded as a phrase or a question.

Answer: FALSE
Page Ref: 127
Topic: Develop your central idea

42) When combined with a central idea, a preview statement can form a "blueprint" of a speech.

Answer: TRUE
Page Ref: 133
Topic: Previewing your main ideas, blueprint

43) List and briefly explain three guidelines to consider when selecting a speech topic.

Page Ref: 117-119
Topic: Guidelines for selecting a topic

44) What is brainstorming? Explain how can it help you in selecting a speech topic? Give a brief example using the topic of "Holidays".

Page Ref: 119-122
Topic: Strategies for selecting a topic

45) Your text explains three general purposes that encompass most public speaking situations. Identify these three and explain what distinguishes them from one another.

Page Ref: 123-124
Topic: Determine your purpose, general purpose

46) Explain how to go about narrowing your topic when it is too broad, using "America" as an example.

Page Ref: 124-130
Topic: Specific purpose, develop central idea

47) What is the difference between a general purpose statement, a specific purpose statement, and a central idea of a speech?

Page Ref: 123-130
Topic: Determine your purpose, develop your central idea

48) Your textbook proposes three guidelines for selecting a speech topic. In a well–developed essay, list and describe each guideline, providing information as to why each is critical to successful speech making.
Page Ref: 117–119
Topic: Guidelines for selecting a topic

49) Using the hypothetical topic, "My Favorite Television Program," develop (1) a general purpose statement; (2) a specific purpose statement in the form of a behavioral objective; and (3) a central idea. Then explain how these three statements will be of benefit in speech preparation.
Page Ref: 123–130
Topic: Determine your purpose, develop your central idea

50) Once you've chosen a topic and sufficiently narrowed it into a workable amount of information for a speech, you must organize the information into main points. What are the three ways your textbook suggests for accomplishing this step in the speech preparation process? Identify and explain each in a well–developed, thorough essay.
Page Ref: 131–133
Topic: Generate and preview your main idea, generating main ideas

Chapter 7 Gathering Supporting Material

1) A vast collection of hundreds of thousands of computers accessible to millions of people all over the world is know as

A) a search engine.

B) the Internet.

C) the World Wide Web.

D) cyberspace.

Answer: B
Page Ref: 140
Topic: The Internet
Skill: Definition Question

2) The address of each Website or Web page is known as

A) the directory location.

B) the URL or uniform resource locator.

C) the hyperlink.

D) the computer address.

Answer: B
Page Ref: 141
Topic: The Internet, the World Wide Web
Skill: Definition Question

3) A site that works much like a traditional card catalog or index, by allowing the user to perform a subject or keyword search is known as

A) a search engine.

B) a hyperlink.

C) a directory.

D) a browser.

Answer: A
Page Ref: 141
Topic: Directories and search engines
Skill: Definition Question

4) Boolean searches on the Internet

A) provide too much information.

B) help narrow your search.

C) look for viruses on your computer.

D) browse broad categories.

Answer: B
Page Ref: 142
Topic: The Internet, directories and search engines
Skill: Definition Question

5) The term "periodicals" refers to

A) books.

B) newspapers.

C) magazines and journals.

D) indexes.

Answer: C
Page Ref: 147
Topic: Library resources, periodicals
Skill: Definition Question

6) A useful Internet index of periodicals, which contains a collection of indexes through a single company is

    A) Reader's Guide to Periodical Literature   B) Social Sciences Index

    C) Humanities Index   D) Info Trac.

Answer: D
Page Ref: 147
Topic: Library resources, periodicals
Skill: Definition Question

7) These databases combine both index and text, allowing you to locate not only bibliographic information, but the resources themselves through a keyword or subject search.

    A) Info Trac   B) Reader's Guide   C) Full-text   D) ERIC

Answer: C
Page Ref: 148
Topic: Library resources, full-text databases
Skill: Definition Question

8) Discussing your speech topic with someone who is knowledgeable on the subject is a method of gathering support material known as

    A) expert testimony.   B) interviewing.

    C) research.   D) peer testimony.

Answer: B
Page Ref: 151
Topic: Interviews
Skill: Definition Question

9) What is the first source of supporting material a speaker should rely upon?

    A) published sources, such as books, magazines, and newspapers

    B) scientific journals that contain reports of current research

    C) dictionaries, encyclopedias, and other reference materials

    D) her or his own personal experience and knowledge

Answer: D
Page Ref: 140
Topic: Personal knowledge and experience
Skill: Description Question

10) What device on the World Wide Web offers a continuous and specific categories of information from which to select?

    A) a directory   B) a browser   C) a hyperlink   D) a bookmark

Answer: A
Page Ref: 141
Topic: The Internet, directories and search engines
Skill: Description Question

11) One way that you can determine if a Web site is authentic and reliable is by:

   A) determining if the site continues to pop up when conducting different Boolean searches under similar topics.

   B) checking to see if the site appears first on the list of search engine hits.

   C) checking the site to see if it is sponsored by an individual or organization that is credible.

   D) noting if the design of the site is advanced and appears reliable.

Answer: C
Page Ref: 142-145
Topic: The Internet, evaluating web resources
Skill: Description Question

12) Libraries' collections of books are generally called

   A) open-stacks.   B) closed-stacks.   C) stashes.   D) stacks.

Answer: D
Page Ref: 146
Topic: Library resources
Skill: Description Question

13) What index has a listing of bibliographical data for articles published in a group of magazines and/or journals during a given time period?

   A) Readers Index   B) Periodical Index

   C) Newspaper Index   D) Full-text Index

Answer: B
Page Ref: 147
Topic: Library resources, periodicals
Skill: Description Question

14) Once you have arranged an interview with an authority on your speech topic, what is your next task?

   A) Ask the interviewee if you may audio- or videotape the interview.

   B) Conduct the interview with your interviewee as professionally as possible.

   C) Plan for the interview by conducting research and planning specific questions.

   D) Determine how you will use the interview information in your speech.

Answer: C
Page Ref: 151-153
Topic: Interviews
Skill: Description Question

15) The use of audio or video recorders can be a liability in an interview because

    A) they are illegal and should never by used when conducting an interview.

    B) they are awkward to handle and more impersonal than note-taking.

    C) some people are more self-conscious and intimidated when being recorded.

    D) the interviewee must sign a consent form before you can begin recording.

Answer: C
Page Ref: 153
Topic: Planning the interview, plan a recording strategy
Skill: Description Question

16) By using the MLA or APA format, the speaker

    A) restricts the possible organizational patterns in the speech.

    B) established a consistent format for citing published sources in the bibliography.

    C) referred to the index or search engine used when researching.

    D) narrowed the topic to a common format.

Answer: B
Page Ref: 155-156
Topic: Research strategies, develop a preliminary bibliography
Skill: Description Question

17) What is "http://www.owens.edu" an example of?

    A) a URL, or uniform resource locator   B) a Web browser

    C) an e-mail address   D) a Web directory

Answer: A
Page Ref: 141
Topic: World Wide Web
Skill: Example Question

18) *Google , Yahoo!,* and *Lycos* are examples of

    A) a domain.   B) a full-text database.

    C) a directory.   D) an Internet browser.

Answer: C
Page Ref: 141
Topic: The Internet, directories and search engines
Skill: Example Question

19) It is necessary to determine what individual or organization is responsible for a Website in order to determine its

    A) accuracy.   B) accountability.   C) objectivity.   D) diversity.

Answer: B
Page Ref: 142-143
Topic: Evaluating Web resources
Skill: Example Question

20) *Academic Search Premier* and *ERIC* are examples of

    A) Web browsers.   B) Web directories.

    C) full-text databases.   D) search engines.

Answer: C
Page Ref: 148
Topic: Library resources, full-text databases
Skill: Example Question

21) Because back issues of newspapers can take up a great deal of space, libraries may safely and efficiently store older copies of the paper

    A) on line for quick access.   B) on microfilm.

    C) in the newspaper index   D) at ABI/Inform for access.

Answer: B
Page Ref: 148
Topic: Library resources, newspapers
Skill: Example Question

22) After your conversation with a representative from the health and wellness program at a local hospital, you organize your notes and decide which statements to quote in your speech. This form of supporting material is termed

    A) firsthand experience.   B) an interview.

    C) research.   D) peer testimony.

Answer: B
Page Ref: 151
Topic: Interviews
Skill: Example Question

23) When setting up a preliminary bibliography, it is necessary to use a consistent format in order to have all the information needed to locate and verify your sources. The two most commonly used formats are

    A) ADA and MLA   B) APA and MLK

    C) MLA and AMA   D) MLA and APA

Answer: D
Page Ref: 156
Topic: Research strategies, develop a preliminary bibliography
Skill: Example Question

24) When listing bibliographic information from an Internet source, include the author and title, if listed, the source and date. Two required citings at the end of a Web documentation are

    A) homepage description and date of access.

    B) URL address and accountability.

    C) date of access and URL address.

    D) accuracy and date of access.

Answer: C
Page Ref: 156–157
Topic: Research strategies, develop a preliminary bibliography
Skill: Example Question

25) Joe is a former world weight lifter and professional body builder. He is preparing an informative speech on the abuse of steroids in physical fitness. Through his personal experiences, what quality can Joe add to the presentation of his speech?

    A) motivation   B) credibility   C) satisfaction   D) persuasion

Answer: B
Page Ref: 140
Topic: Personal knowledge and experience
Skill: Application Question

26) You want to give an informative speech on politics in the Middle East, but, realizing that there is so much information, you become overwhelmed. According to advice from your textbook, where should you start?

    A) You should start with traditional library sources, because they are much more reliable than Web sources.

    B) You should first conduct a personal interview with someone knowledgeable on the topic; then follow that up with traditional library research.

    C) You should use a browser to help you navigate the World Wide Web, because browsers can sort broad-based information into specific categories.

    D) You should use a directory or search engine on the World Wide Web to help you locate current and relevant information on the topic.

Answer: D
Page Ref: 141
Topic: The Internet, directories and search engines
Skill: Application Question

27) Jack used primarily Web sources for his informative speech about gun control. However, his over-reliance on the Web site sponsored by the National Rifle Association caused his speech to be slanted in one direction, rather than presenting multiple sides of the issue. Which of the six criteria for evaluating Web sources did Jack ignore?

    A) accountability   B) accuracy   C) objectivity   D) usability

Answer: C
Page Ref: 144
Topic: Evaluating Web resources
Skill: Application Question

28) Kenisha decided to write her persuasive speech on "Human Cloning." She didn't feel comfortable using Internet sources and so relied on books and material from a class she had taken last year. What is the problem with Kenisha's research?

   A) Nothing; books are always the best and most reliable source for any topic.

   B) Kenisha needed to interview someone about this subject as well as use the books.

   C) Kenisha should have researched newspapers and periodicals for the most recent material.

   D) Nothing: it is not necessary to use the Internet to find the most updated material.

   Answer: C
   Page Ref: 147–149
   Topic: Library resources
   Skill: Application Question

29) Carl is researching a speech on euthanasia. He knows that there are some excellent journal articles on the subject, but his university's small library doesn't carry the journals in which the articles appear. Carl has only a few days until he must give the speech; what should he do?

   A) Carl should use interlibrary loan to see if he can locate the needed journal articles.

   B) Carl waited too late to start his research, so he'll have to use something else instead of the journal articles.

   C) Carl should substitute Web site information for the journal articles, because material from the Web is more accurate and current than published journal articles.

   D) Carl should use a full-text database, like *Academic Search Premier*, to attempt to locate complete texts of the journal articles.

   Answer: D
   Page Ref: 148
   Topic: Library resources, full-text databases
   Skill: Application Question

30) For her speech about toxic waste dumping, Claire sets up an interview with a campus professor who has conducted extensive research on the subject. As her first question, she asked the professor, "Why doesn't the college do something about toxic waste dumping on property owned by the college?" Which of the following statements best identifies the problem here?

   A) Claire should have known never to ask hostile questions in an interview.

   B) Claire made a mistake in not having enough background information about the subject.

   C) Claire made a mistake by not asking "soft" questions, before going to the "hard" ones.

   D) Claire was not at fault; an interviewer needs to get tough in order to get the real answers.

   Answer: C
   Page Ref: 153
   Topic: Interviews, planning the interview
   Skill: Application Question

31) Marcie was conducting an interview with the local homeless shelter supervisor. The supervisor kept answering "Yes" or "No" to all of Marcie's questions. Marcie was getting frustrated because she was not getting the material she needed. What was the problem here?

   A) Marcie was not at fault; the supervisor was just close minded and not helpful.

   B) Marcie had planned only closed-ended questions and forgot to follow up by asking "Why?"

   C) The supervisor was probably new and inexperienced and didn't know the answers.

   D) The text doesn't have a suggestion for this; it's just one of those awkward things that happens.

   Answer: B
   Page Ref: 153-154
   Topic: Planning the interview
   Skill: Application Question

32) Tracie is gathering sources of support for her persuasive speech on animal testing for medical purposes. She makes use of Web sources and has a great deal of relevant material. However, when outlining the speech, she can't find the source of many of the facts and statistics she plans to use. What is Tracie's problem?

   A) Tracie forgot to get full citations on her sources, but she can orally cite what she remembers.

   B) Tracie needed a preliminary bibliography with all necessary material to locate the sources.

   C) Tracie violated a principle of outlining,; never insert supporting material into an outline for a speech.

   D) Tracie doesn't have a problem; the audience trusts her to be truthful and not make up facts.

   Answer: B
   Page Ref: 155-157
   Topic: Research strategies, develop a preliminary bibliography
   Skill: Application Question

33) Personal knowledge often has the disadvantage of lowering your credibility because the audience doesn't know if you're knowledgeable about that topic.

   Answer: FALSE
   Page Ref: 140
   Topic: Personal knowledge and experience

34) When planning a speech, you should always begin by considering your personal experience and knowledge.

   Answer: TRUE
   Page Ref: 140
   Topic: Personal knowledge and experience

35) A browser and a search engine serve the same function on the Web.

Answer: FALSE
Page Ref: 141
Topic: The Internet, directories and search engines

36) Often it is hard to find enough material to support a speech on the Internet.

Answer: FALSE
Page Ref: 141
Topic: The Internet, directories and search engines

37) When you evaluate a Web source by finding out all you can about the sponsor of the source, you are using the textbook standard termed accuracy.

Answer: FALSE
Page Ref: 143-144
Topic: Evaluating Web resources

38) The domain address ".org" always indicates nonprofit groups.

Answer: TRUE
Page Ref: 143
Topic: Evaluating Web resources

39) The more objective the author, the more credible the facts and information presented.

Answer: TRUE
Page Ref: 144
Topic: Objectivity

40) When checking a Web site for diversity, be sure there is no bias against any ethnic, racial, gender, or sexual-preference group.

Answer: TRUE
Page Ref: 144
Topic: Diversity

41) Open-stacks give researchers the chance to make lucky finds because books on a particular subject are shelved next to one another.

Answer: TRUE
Page Ref: 146
Topic: Library resources, books

42) When planning an interview, it is a good idea to keep your questions spontaneous.

Answer: FALSE
Page Ref: 152-153
Topic: Interviews, planning the interview

43) Define and briefly explain each of the following: Website, browser, directory, and search engine.
Page Ref: 140-142
Topic: The Internet

44) Explain why the textbook might issue a word of caution when setting up interviews. Give an example.
Page Ref: 151
Topic: Interviews

45) There are a number of resources available for speakers when preparing for a speech. Briefly explain the strengths and weaknesses of the following: Books, periodicals, newspapers, full-text databases, and government documents.
Page Ref: 145-151
Topic: Library resources

46) Assume that you will be conducting a personal interview with an authority on your speech topic, as a form of supporting material. How would you go about planning the interview?
Page Ref: 152-154
Topic: Interviews, planning the interview

47) What information is necessary when composing a bibliography for a Web source?
Page Ref: 155-157
Topic: Research strategies, develop a preliminary bibliography

48) Name and explain the importance of applying each of the six criteria, suggested by your text, for evaluating Web sources.
Page Ref: 142-145
Topic: The Internet, evaluating web resources

49) If you are preparing a speech on "Job and career trends within in the United States in the last 10 years," what four sources of information could possibly be utilized as supporting material? Be specific and vary your selections according to Internet and traditional library materials identified in your text. Offer clear explanations as to why each source would be beneficial.
Page Ref: 140-155
Topic: Gathering supporting material

50) In a well-developed essay, explain what should occur in the process of conducting an interview with an authority on a speech topic, as well as in the follow-up phase.
Page Ref: 151-154
Topic: Interviews

Chapter 8 Supporting Your Speech

1) A lengthy illustration with a plot—beginning, climatic point, and end—is called
   A) a hypothetical illustration.   B) a brief illustration.
   C) an extended illustration.   D) a literal illustration.

   Answer: C
   Page Ref: 169
   Topic: Illustrations, extended illustrations
   Skill: Definition Question

2) A short illustration which is no longer than a sentence or two is called
   A) a hypothetical illustration.   B) an explanation.
   C) a brief illustration.   D) a literal illustration.

   Answer: C
   Page Ref: 169
   Topic: Illustrations, brief illustrations
   Skill: Definition Question

3) An illustration that includes the word "imagine", or presents a scenario that *might* happen, is
   A) a hypothetical illustration.   B) an extended illustration.
   C) a definition.   D) an explanation.

   Answer: A
   Page Ref: 170
   Topic: Illustrations, hypothetical illustrations
   Skill: Definition Question

4) A statement that makes clear how something is done or why it exists in its present or past form
   is known as a(n)
   A) definition.   B) explanation.   C) image.   D) analogy.

   Answer: B
   Page Ref: 171
   Topic: Descriptions and explanations
   Skill: Definition Question

5) When it is necessary in a speech to explain a term that the audience might not understand,
   look in a dictionary such as *Webster's* for
   A) a definition by classification.   B) an operational definition.
   C) an original definition.   D) an analogical definition.

   Answer: A
   Page Ref: 173
   Topic: Definitions, definitions by classification
   Skill: Definition Question

6) A figurative analogy is

    A) a form of proof.   B) a comparison of things actually similar.

    C) not usually used in speeches.   D) in the form of a metaphor or simile.

Answer: D
Page Ref: 175–176
Topic: Analogies
Skill: Definition Question

7) When someone, who is a recognized authority in a specialized area, states his/her opinion, this is considered

    A) expert testimony.   B) lay testimony.

    C) a literary quotation.   D) individual opinion.

Answer: A
Page Ref: 180
Topic: Opinions, expert testimony
Skill: Definition Question

8) A mother of two children who speaks about the death of her child due to influenza is giving a

    A) lay testimony.   B) expert testimony.

    C) factual material.   D) unbiased testimony.

Answer: A
Page Ref: 180
Topic: Opinions, lay testimony
Skill: Definition Question

9) When using brief illustrations, it is often stronger to use

    A) only one at a time, throughout your speech.

    B) those that are not personal.

    C) a series of brief illustrations.

    D) them only in the introduction or conclusion.

Answer: C
Page Ref: 169
Topic: Illustrations, brief illustrations
Skill: Description Question

10) What does your textbook advise regarding the use of hypothetical illustrations in a speech?

   A) Using a series of hypothetical illustrations can often have more impact than a single illustration.

   B) Make sure your audience knows from the beginning that your illustration is hypothetical.

   C) A hypothetical illustration is only effective if it is lengthy; brief hypotheticals are ineffective.

   D) Hypothetical illustrations are fine in a conclusion, but shouldn't be used in the body of a speech.

Answer: B
Page Ref: 170
Topic: Illustrations, hypothetical illustrations
Skill: Description Question

11) Using sensory information, or "word pictures", which allows your audience to mentally see, hear, smell, touch, or taste something is a process known as

   A) explanation.   B) description.   C) definition.   D) illustration.

Answer: B
Page Ref: 171-172
Topic: Descriptions and explanations, describing
Skill: Description Question

12) If, as supporting material for a speech, you discuss or demonstrate a process of any kind, you are

   A) explaining why.   B) explaining how.

   C) describing.   D) defining.

Answer: B
Page Ref: 172
Topic: Descriptions and explanations, explaining how
Skill: Description Question

13) What are important guidelines for the use of statistics in a speech?

   A) Use reputable, authoritative, unbiased sources for your statistics.

   B) Use statistics that are mainly from secondary sources.

   C) Use as many statistics as you can find because they enhance credibility.

   D) Report a statistic down to the last decimal point, to be thorough and accurate.

Answer: A
Page Ref: 177
Topic: Statistics, using statistics effectively
Skill: Description Question

14) Government agencies, independent survey organizations, or scholarly research reports can be considered reliable sources because they are

    A) reputable.   B) accessible.   C) effective.   D) varied.

Answer: A
Page Ref: 177
Topic: Statistics, using statistics effectively
Skill: Description Question

15) When is it a good idea to use expert testimony in a speech?

    A) when your topic requires that you make predictions

    B) when your topic is informative

    C) when your topic is humorous

    D) when your topic is dull

Answer: A
Page Ref: 180
Topic: Opinions, expert testimony
Skill: Description Question

16) When using a literary quotation as supporting material, it is best to

    A) say "quote" and "unquote."   B) be sure and keep the quote brief.

    C) make them long and important.   D) try to find quotes that are new.

Answer: B
Page Ref: 180
Topic: Opinions, literary quotations
Skill: Description Question

17) The statement, "Years ago when we were kids, my friends and I never thought twice about tossing trash out into the street from our car windows. Now most of us wouldn't even think about littering like this," is a form of supporting material termed

    A) a brief illustration.   B) an extended illustration.

    C) a hypothetical illustration.   D) an analogy.

Answer: A
Page Ref: 169
Topic: Illustrations, brief illustrations
Skill: Example Question

18) "Sarah Hughes is the future of figure skating in America. She has an elegance far beyond her years, combined with a dazzling athletic ability." This statement is a form of supporting material known as

    A) a description.   B) an explanation.   C) a definition.   D) an illustration.

Answer: A
Page Ref: 171–172
Topic: Descriptions and explanations, describing
Skill: Example Question

19) Fernando's speech statement, "Hamas is an Arabic acronym for the Islamic Resistance Movement, a Palestinian Islamic fundamentalist organization established in 1987. It is an offshoot of the Muslim Brotherhood which has carried out numerous terrorist attacks on Israelis," is a form of supporting material known as

    A) a brief illustration.   B) an analogy.

    C) a definition.   D) a description.

Answer: C
Page Ref: 173
Topic: Definitions
Skill: Example Question

20) What form of supporting material is being utilized in the following question: "If many states profit from the institution of a lottery, why can't our home state do the same?"

    A) an extended analogy   B) a figurative analogy

    C) a literal analogy   D) a faulty analogy

Answer: C
Page Ref: 175
Topic: Analogies, literal analogies
Skill: Example Question

21) Cass cited *The National Enquirer* as a source for a statistic she used on her speech about UFOs. Does this meet the text's guidelines for using statistics effectively in a speech?

    A) Yes; she used this information as a primary source within her speech.

    B) Yes, as long as she gave a complete citation for the publication, including date and author name.

    C) No; she violated the guideline which states that you must use reliable sources for statistics.

    D) No; she should have only used books because they are the most current sources.

Answer: C
Page Ref: 177
Topic: Statistics, using statistics effectively
Skill: Example Question

22) In her speech about cancer, Bonnie included information from a friend's mother who had undergone chemotherapy and whose cancer was in remission. Was this appropriate supporting material for the speech?

    A) Yes; the information from the friend's mother was considered lay testimony about cancer.

    B) No; Bonnie should have only used experts on the subject, not someone who experienced cancer.

    C) Yes, but only as long as the friend's mother was considered an "expert" on cancer.

    D) No; the friend's mother was anything but an "unbiased" authority on the subject.

Answer: A
Page Ref: 180
Topic: Opinions, lay testimony
Skill: Example Question

23) Richard says in his speech, "In the words of Franklin D. Roosevelt, 'The only thing we have to fear, is fear itself.'" What form of supporting material is Richard employing?

    A) expert testimony   B) lay testimony

    C) figurative quotation   D) literary quotation

Answer: D
Page Ref: 180
Topic: Opinions, literary quotations
Skill: Example Question

24) In his speech about date rape on college campuses, Ryan cites statistics from state and county law enforcement documents; then he includes statistics from incidents on his own campus. Which principle of selecting the best supporting material is Ryan using?

    A) proximity   B) suitability   C) variety   D) concreteness

Answer: A
Page Ref: 183
Topic: Selecting the best supporting material
Skill: Example Question

25) "According to an Associated Press article from February 2004, Houston police found more than 3,200 stolen vehicles--mostly from Texas, California, and Florida--in Guatemala by tracing vehicle identification numbers through a Guatemalan database." This type of supporting material in a speech is termed

    A) a brief illustration.   B) an extended illustration.

    C) a statistic.   D) expert testimony.

Answer: A
Page Ref: 169
Topic: Illustrations, brief illustrations
Skill: Application Question

26) In his speech about drinking and driving, David told the story of what happened to three friends of his. He went into detail about how they had been partying, how they wouldn't let anyone sober drive them home, and how their lives ended when the car they were in wrapped around a tree in the middle of the night. What kind of supporting material did David use in his speech?

A) a brief illustration

B) an extended illustration

C) a statistic

D) expert testimony

Answer: B
Page Ref: 169
Topic: Illustrations, extended illustrations
Skill: Application Question

27) Samantha is giving a speech on binge drinking. She uses supporting material that says, "A binge drinker is a man who drinks five or more drinks in one sitting or a woman who drinks four." This type of supporting material is

A) an illustration.   B) an opinion.   C) an analogy.   D) a definition.

Answer: D
Page Ref: 173
Topic: Definitions
Skill: Application Question

28) In a persuasive speech, you compared stem cell research to abortion on the basis that they are both destroying human life. In this case you were using

A) a literal analogy

B) a figurative analogy

C) an extended illustration

D) a brief example

Answer: A
Page Ref: 175
Topic: Analogies, literal analogies
Skill: Application Question

29) In her speech about the benefits of vehicle air bags, Gretta states: "Based on information gathered from 1987 to 2003, The National Highway Traffic Safety Administration estimates that 13,967 people are alive today because of their vehicle airbags. Almost 14,000 people! That would be the equivalent of the full-time students attending this college. Imagine, all those lives saved by a simple airbag." What guideline about the use of statistics is Gretta following in her speech?

A) interpreting statistics accurately

B) making statistics understandable and memorable

C) using secondary sources

D) using visual aids to present statistics

Answer: B
Page Ref: 178
Topic: Statistics, using statistics effectively
Skill: Application Question

30) When Selena said, in her speech about women's rights, "Just like Sojourner Truth said over 150 years ago, 'If the first woman God ever made was strong enough to turn the world upside down all alone, these women together ought to be able to turn it back, and get it right side up again! And now they is asking to do it, the men better let them.'" What form of supporting material was she using?

    A) expert statistics, because Sojourner Truth was an expert on women's rights

    B) a literary analogy, because Selena compared sexism today with sexism 150 years ago

    C) a literary quotation from Sojourner Truth's famous speech

    D) a brief illustration about sexism now, versus 150 years ago

Answer: C
Page Ref: 180
Topic: Opinions, literary quotations
Skill: Application Question

31) In his persuasive speech, Li used several illustrations—some brief, some extended, and some hypothetical. He decided that this form of supporting material would be more powerful and memorable than dry statistics or definitions. Which of the following statements best applies to this situation?

    A) Li made a good decision because illustrations are the most effective form of supporting material.

    B) Li followed the text's advice about using multiple forms of illustrations as his main source of supporting material.

    C) Li's over-reliance on illustrations shows that he ignored the text's advice about selecting supporting material that has proximity to the audience.

    D) Li's over-reliance on illustrations shows that he ignored the text's advice about using a variety of types of supporting material.

Answer: D
Page Ref: 183
Topic: Selecting the best supporting material
Skill: Application Question

32) When Jessica cited the number of people dying everyday in Sudan's civil war, her audience responded apathetically. Jessica made every attempt to support her topic in provocative, ethical ways, but just couldn't seem to elicit the interest she wanted from her listeners. What textbook suggestion regarding the use of supporting material best relates to this situation?

    A) The statistics weren't of enough magnitude to generate audience interest.

    B) The statistics and vivid descriptions weren't suitable to Jessica's topic.

    C) The information may not have had enough proximity to people's lives to generate interest.

    D) Jessica's information was vague and abstract, which lost the attention of her audience.

Answer: C
Page Ref: 183
Topic: Selecting the best supporting material
Skill: Application Question

33) A skilled public speaker must learn to choose and use a variety of supporting material.

Answer: TRUE
Page Ref: 168
Topic: Supporting your speech

34) The best types of illustrations are those that are not personal to the speaker.

Answer: FALSE
Page Ref: 168-169
Topic: Illustrations

35) In a speech, the longer and more detailed the illustration, the greater the possibility of confusing the audience.

Answer: FALSE
Page Ref: 169
Topic: Illustrations, extended illustrations

36) It is best to inform your audience that your illustration is hypothetical because doing so will allow the audience to imagine themselves in a particular situation.

Answer: TRUE
Page Ref: 170
Topic: Illustrations, hypothetical illustrations

37) In choosing illustrations, it is better to find those that are not typical.

Answer: FALSE
Page Ref: 170
Topic: Using illustrations effectively

38) Explanations should have vivid and specific language in order to capture and hold the attention of your audience.

Answer: TRUE
Page Ref: 170
Topic: Using illustrations effectively

39) In explaining "why," a speaker can set up the causes for a cause-solution speech.

Answer: TRUE
Page Ref: 172-173
Topic: Descriptions and explanations, explaining why

40) A strategy to captivate audiences instantly is to begin a speech with a definition -- no matter the level of the word.

Answer: FALSE
Page Ref: 173
Topic: Definitions

41) When speaking to an audience from another culture, it is a good strategy to use literal analogies that compare your message to something specific in their culture.

Answer: TRUE
Page Ref: 175
Topic: Analogies, literal analogies

42) Lay testimony is preferable to expert testimony because of its personal impact on an audience.

Answer: FALSE
Page Ref: 180
Topic: Opinions, lay testimony

43) Briefly define the following and give an original example for support: brief illustration, extended illustration, hypothetical illustration.

Page Ref: 168-170
Topic: Illustrations

44) Using the hypothetical speech topic of the prevalence of binge drinking in the college population, explain how supporting material in the form of a brief illustration, an explanation, and a statistic could be used in the speech.

Page Ref: 168-179
Topic: Supporting your speech

45) Discuss the difference between description and explanation. Give a brief example of each.

Page Ref: 171-173
Topic: Descriptions and explanations

46) What is the difference between definitions by classification and operational definitions? How could each be used in a speech?

Page Ref: 173-174
Topic: Definitions

47) Discuss the difference between a literal and a figurative analogy. Give an example of each.

Page Ref: 175-176
Topic: Analogies

48) Using the hypothetical speech topic, "Should hand guns be owned only by police officers in the United States," describe four different sources of supporting material that could be effectively incorporated into this speech. Back up your choices with clear reasons, that is, argue effectively as to why certain materials are better than others for this topic.

Page Ref: 183
Topic: Selecting the best supporting material

49) Describe how opinions can be used as supporting material. Determine the specific purposes and advantages, as well as touching on the disadvantages, of the different types of opinions.

Page Ref: 179-182
Topic: Opinions

50) If you have more material than you can possibly use when constructing your speech, you can use the six criteria listed in the text to make sure you choose the best supporting material. Use a speech that you have created as an example and illustrate what strategies you used while preparing your speech and which of the six criteria might have helped make your information more effective.

Page Ref: 183
Topic: Selecting the best supporting material

Chapter 9 Organizing Your Speech

1) The method a speaker uses to arrange her or his main ideas is termed
    A) the organizational pattern.   B) the speaking outline.
    C) the preliminary outline.   D) the last resort.

Answer: A
Page Ref: 189
Topic: Organizing your main ideas
Skill: Definition Question

2) Organizing ideas within a speech according to the order in which they occurred or should occur employs
    A) a topical pattern.   B) a chronological pattern.
    C) a spatial pattern.   D) a cause–effect pattern.

Answer: B
Page Ref: 189
Topic: Organizing main ideas, arranging ideas spatially
Skill: Definition Question

3) Organizing speech ideas according to direction and location is
    A) a topical pattern.   B) a chronological pattern.
    C) a spatial pattern.   D) a cause–effect pattern

Answer: C
Page Ref: 192
Topic: Organizing main ideas, organizing ideas spatially
Skill: Definition Question

4) If a speech is organized to identify a situation and then discuss the impact of that situation occurring, the speaker has used
    A) a topical pattern.   B) a chronological pattern.
    C) a cause–effect pattern.   D) a spatial pattern.

Answer: C
Page Ref: 193
Topic: Organizing main ideas, organizing to show cause and effect
Skill: Definition Question

5) A speech topic that presents an issue that needs resolving can effectively be organized as
    A) cause–effect.   B) recency pattern.
    C) problem-solution.   D) chronological.

Answer: C
Page Ref: 194
Topic: Organizing main ideas, organizing by problem and solution
Skill: Definition Question

6) When you present the most important or convincing idea first in your speech, you are using the principle of

    A) primacy.   B) specificity.   C) complexity.   D) recency.

Answer: A
Page Ref: 199
Topic: Organizing supporting materials, primacy or recency
Skill: Definition Question

7) Words and gestures, that allow you to move smoothly from one idea to the next throughout the speech, are known as

    A) relevant movements.   B) nonverbals.

    C) supports.   D) signposts.

Answer: D
Page Ref: 201–202
Topic: Developing signposts
Skill: Definition Question

8) Transitions, previews, and summaries are all examples of

    A) signposts.   B) main ideas.

    C) supporting material.   D) organization.

Answer: A
Page Ref: 201–202
Topic: Developing signposts
Skill: Definition Question

9) Telling your audience your main ideas before you begin to develop your speech is a

    A) a summary statement.   B) a connector.

    C) a preview.   D) a verbal transition.

Answer: C
Page Ref: 203
Topic: Developing signposts, previews
Skill: Definition Question

10) In addition to using a preview at the beginning of the speech, speakers can use _____ previews at various points throughout the speech.

    A) miniature   B) internal   C) spatial   D) summative

Answer: B
Page Ref: 204
Topic: Developing signposts, previews
Skill: Definition Question

11) A speech organizational pattern which goes one step beyond cause and effect to discuss ways to alter, fix, or correct an effect is termed

    A) the motivated sequence.   B) a problem-solution pattern.

    C) an extended cause-effect pattern.   D) a chronological pattern.

Answer: B
Page Ref: 194
Topic: Organizing main ideas, organizing by problem and solution
Skill: Description Question

12) After speakers have organized their main points, what is the next step?

    A) arranging points into a logical, effective pattern

    B) attaching supporting material to the main points

    C) dividing main points into subpoints

    D) finding sources of support for main points

Answer: C
Page Ref: 196
Topic: Subdividing main ideas
Skill: Description Question

13) When you state a main idea, cite the source, present the material, and then explain how the material supports the main idea, you are

    A) using the recency principle properly.

    B) presenting an internal preview.

    C) integrating supporting materials smoothly.

    D) overstating your main ideas.

Answer: C
Page Ref: 197-198
Topic: Integrating your supporting materials
Skill: Description Question

14) The main reason to use previews, summaries, and signposts is to

    A) keep your speech simple so you don't get confused.

    B) keep your audience on track with your speech.

    C) make the speech long enough to fill the time period.

    D) make sure you completely cover your topic.

Answer: B
Page Ref: 201-202
Topic: Developing signposts
Skill: Description Question

15) Words and phrases, such as "In addition," "In other words," and "Therefore," are examples of

A) verbal signpost.
B) organizational material.
C) nonverbal signpost.
D) summary statements.

Answer: A
Page Ref: 202
Topic: Developing signposts, transitions
Skill: Description Question

16) A planned pause in a speech may be used as

A) a time to catch your breath.
B) a nonverbal signpost.
C) an internal preview.
D) an effective filler.

Answer: B
Page Ref: 202-203
Topic: Developing signposts, transitions
Skill: Description Question

17) When explaining the progress of molecular discoveries, Shanthani began by discussing Mendel's 1866 studies about inheritance of biological traits in peas, ending with recent information about the human genome project. Which pattern of organization would best suit Shanthani's speech?

A) topical   B) spatial   C) chronological   D) cause-effect

Answer: C
Page Ref: 189
Topic: Organizing main ideas, arranging ideas spatially
Skill: Example Question

18) For her informative speech, Abegail wanted to tell her audience what they need to consider when purchasing a new computer. Which organizational pattern lends itself best to this topic?

A) topical   B) spatial   C) chronological   D) cause-effect

Answer: A
Page Ref: 191
Topic: Organizing main ideas, organizing ideas topically
Skill: Example Question

19) Deanna makes the claim in her persuasive speech that unregulated car emissions in major urban areas worldwide contribute to the depletion of the ozone layer, which contributes to global warming. Which type of organizational pattern is reflected in this example?

A) cause-effect
B) topical
C) problem-solution
D) spatial

Answer: A
Page Ref: 193
Topic: Organizing ideas to show cause and effect
Skill: Example Question

20) Brayden wanted his audience to understand that the increased parking fees were beneficial to the students, faculty, and college as a whole for two main reasons. He was using the _____ organizational pattern to present his information.

    A) spatial   B) chronological

    C) solution–problem   D) topical

Answer: C
Page Ref: 194
Topic: Organizing main ideas, organizing by problem and solution
Skill: Example Question

21) "An article in the January, 2002 issue of *Newsweek* about the failure of Enron asserts, 'Many of Enron's 20,000 employees lost their retirement savings when the company collapsed...By contrast, chairman Ken Lay made $205 million in stock option profits in the past four years alone,...'" This is an example of

    A) a statement of a main idea in a speech.

    B) a subpoint in support of a main idea in a speech.

    C) a citation of supporting material.

    D) a restatement of a main idea in a speech.

Answer: C
Page Ref: 197–198
Topic: Integrating your supporting materials
Skill: Example Question

22) Paul describes first how hunger is a world-wide problem; he then explains that there is a hunger problem in America; then he describes a family suffering in his home town. What aspect of supporting material organization is Paul employing here?

    A) the primacy-recency principle   B) the complexity principle

    C) the "soft" to "hard" evidence principle   D) the specificity principle

Answer: D
Page Ref: 199–200
Topic: Organizing supporting materials, specificity
Skill: Example Question

23) In his speech on varying explanations of how the earth came into existence, Eduardo begins with opinions, moves to inferences, and uses scientific facts in support of his last point. What principle of supporting material organization is Eduardo reflecting in his speech?

    A) primacy-recency   B) "soft" to "hard" evidence

    C) complexity   D) specificity

Answer: B
Page Ref: 200–201
Topic: Organizing supporting materials, "soft" to "hard" evidence
Skill: Example Question

24) Throughout John's speech on the environment, he reviewed and re-emphasized points previously discussed. What is the textbook term for this technique?

   A) internal summary   B) transition

   C) preview   D) external summary

   Answer: A
   Page Ref: 205
   Topic: Developing signposts, summaries
   Skill: Example Question

25) In her presentation to the school board about plans for the new physical fitness facility, Miss. Anderson described the various workout areas, gyms, locker rooms, and physical therapy facilities. Which organizational pattern was Miss. Anderson using in her presentation?

   A) topical   B) spatial

   C) problem-solution   D) chronological

   Answer: B
   Page Ref: 192
   Topic: Organizing main ideas, organizing ideas spatially
   Skill: Application Question

26) Bianca began her speech with a vivid description of the typical waiting area in an emergency room of a public hospital. After completing the description, she began to discuss why emergency rooms have come to represent a critical problem within the health care system. What organizational pattern can you detect in Bianca's speech?

   A) chronological   B) spatial   C) topical   D) cause–effect

   Answer: D
   Page Ref: 193
   Topic: Organizing main ideas, organizing to show cause and effect
   Skill: Application Question

27) Jason says in his speech: "Drug abuse in America's cities is on the rise every day. About 20% more elementary school kids get hooked on narcotics today than in the 1960s. So, we can easily see that we've got a big problem. Now let's talk about what we can do about it." What is Jason's error here?

   A) Jason failed to explain his main idea before citing a statistic.

   B) Jason failed to make his supporting material dramatic enough for the audience.

   C) Jason failed to cite the source of his supporting material.

   D) Jason made no mistake; he used a clear, dramatic statistic in support of his point.

   Answer: C
   Page Ref: 197-198
   Topic: Integrating your supporting materials
   Skill: Application Question

28) Janine organized her three statistics on organ transplants according to their significance. She saved her "clincher" point—about how easy it is to indicate your willingness to donate by signing the back of your driver's license—for the last point before her conclusion. What pattern of supporting material did Janine demonstrate in this speech?

    A) complexity   B) specificity   C) primacy   D) recency

Answer: D
Page Ref: 199
Topic: Organizing supporting materials, primacy or recency
Skill: Application Question

29) For your persuasive speech supporting assisted suicide, you decide to first provide a definition of the term and talk generally about the current status of the problem. Then you will bring up individual incidences in which assisted suicides have prevented needless suffering in the victim, while the family member who assisted has been imprisoned. Which strategy of support material organization is this plan reflecting?

    A) complexity   B) specificity

    C) primacy   D) "soft" to "hard" evidence

Answer: B
Page Ref: 199–200
Topic: Organizing supporting materials, specificity
Skill: Application Question

30) Mandy's "save the whales" speech was very effective because she started off with some stories about whales, then she moved into facts, statistics, and sources. Which principle of support material organization did Mandy effectively use in her speech?

    A) complexity   B) specificity

    C) primacy   D) "soft" to "hard" evidence

Answer: D
Page Ref: 200–201
Topic: Organizing supporting materials, "soft" to "hard" evidence
Skill: Application Question

31) In Daryl's speech on football, he tells the audience in the introduction that he is going to discuss the history of the sport, some of the rules, and the benefits of playing football on cardiovascular fitness. What type of signpost is Daryl demonstrating?

    A) a transition   B) a preview

    C) an internal summary   D) an external summary

Answer: B
Page Ref: 203–204
Topic: Developing signposts, previews
Skill: Application Question

32) In a speech, April says: "You should now understand the three most-recommended methods for improving your ability to recall people's names: the repetition method, the word-association method, and the visual imagery method. I hope you will put these methods into practice and you will remember my name the next time you see me in the hall." What device is April making use of in her speech?

A) a transition

B) a preview statement

C) an internal summary

D) a final summary

Answer: D
Page Ref: 204–205
Topic: Developing signposts, summaries
Skill: Application Question

33) Before organizing your main points, it is wise to review the logical divisions, reasons, or series of steps you identified when you narrowed your topic.

Answer: TRUE
Page Ref: 189
Topic: Organizing your main ideas

34) Speeches on how to do something or how to make something usually use a topical organizational pattern.

Answer: FALSE
Page Ref: 191
Topic: Organizing main ideas, organizing ideas topically

35) Historical speeches and how-to speeches are two kinds of speeches usually organized spatially.

Answer: FALSE
Page Ref: 192-193
Topic: Organizing main ideas, arranging ideas spatially

36) In a speech organized in a cause-effect pattern, the cause must be covered first.

Answer: FALSE
Page Ref: 193-194
Topic: Organizing main ideas, organizing to show cause and effect

37) Stating a problem, discussing its causes, and the emphasizing how best to solve the problem pertains most directly to the problem-solution pattern of arranging points.

Answer: TRUE
Page Ref: 194-195
Topic: Organizing main ideas, organizing by problem and solution

38) Most cultures tend to organize and process information in a linear pattern.

Answer: FALSE
Page Ref: 195
Topic: Organizing main ideas, acknowledging cultural differences

39) It is generally a good idea to assemble supporting material by beginning with the simplest thoughts and working up to the complex ideas.

Answer: TRUE
Page Ref: 200
Topic: Organizing supporting materials, complexity

40) Specificity means that you can organize your supporting material either from general to specific, or from specific to general.

Answer: TRUE
Page Ref: 199
Topic: Organizing supporting materials, specificity

41) The principle of recency means that an audience will best remember your last supporting point.

Answer: TRUE
Page Ref: 199
Topic: Organizing supporting materials, primacy or recency

42) Using visuals as aids to verbal signposts will improve your audience's ability to follow your speech.

Answer: TRUE
Page Ref: 201-202
Topic: Developing signposts

43) Using the hypothetical topic, "Travel in the United States," select an organizational pattern from the ones described in your text. Then defend why this pattern would be best suited for this particular topic.

Page Ref: 189-195
Topic: Organizing your main ideas

44) Define each of the following and give a brief example: cause–effect organization, effect–cause organization, and problem–solution organization

Page Ref: 193-195
Topic: Organizing ideas cause & effect, problem and solution

45) With an original example, explain how to smoothly integrate supporting materials into a speech.

Page Ref: 197-198
Topic: Integrating your supporting materials

46) Briefly explain: (1) primacy–recency principle; (2) specificity principle; (3) complexity principle; and (4) "soft" to "hard" evidence principle.

Page Ref: 198-201
Topic: Organizing supporting materials

47) List and explain the three main signposts discussed in your text. Give an example of each.
Page Ref: 201–205
Topic: Developing signposts

48) Identify and explain the five organizational patterns discussed in your text. Be sure to include what is considered to be the main identifying characteristic of each pattern.
Page Ref: 189–195
Topic: Organizing your main ideas

49) In any speech, your research material must be organized in order to best support your main ideas. Your text discusses five strategies that will help you decide how to order this material. Using the topic "Always Wear Your Seat Belt" name three of these strategies, and illustrate how you might use them in the above speech.
Page Ref: 198–201
Topic: Organizing supporting materials

50) In a speech entitled "How to Build a Bat House," name and give specific examples of how different types of signposts could be used in order to help your audience understand and remember your speech.
Page Ref: 201–205
Topic: Developing signposts

Chapter 10 Introducing and Concluding Your Speech

1) Every speech you give will have three basic parts; the first part is
    A) the specific purpose.   B) the summary.
    C) the introduction.   D) the central idea.

Answer: C
Page Ref: 212
Topic: Introductions
Skill: Definition Question

2) The first step in an introduction is
    A) to reveal the topic.   B) a preview of main ideas.
    C) to get the audience's attention.   D) to establish credibility.

Answer: C
Page Ref: 213
Topic: Purposes of introductions
Skill: Definition Question

3) In an introduction, proximity is
    A) how close the speaker is to the audience.
    B) using the most current information.
    C) assuring the thesis statement is the first idea presented.
    D) using information that affects the audience directly.

Answer: D
Page Ref: 214
Topic: Purposes of introductions
Skill: Definition Question

4) Credibility is
    A) the attitude listeners hold toward a speaker.
    B) the value listeners give the topic.
    C) is something that all speakers possess.
    D) established with the specific purpose of the speech.

Answer: A
Page Ref: 214
Topic: Purposes of introductions, establish your credibility
Skill: Definition Question

5) It is important in an introduction to build trust with the audience, to have them believe you and like you. This is known as speaker

    A) likability.   B) credibility.

    C) trustworthiness.   D) popularity.

Answer: B
Page Ref: 214
Topic: Purposes of introductions, establish your credibility
Skill: Definition Question

6) This signpost may enumerate the ideas and points that will be presented in the speech. This signpost is known as

    A) a summary.   B) a specific purpose.

    C) a preview.   D) an emphasis statement.

Answer: C
Page Ref: 215
Topic: Purposes of introductions, preview your main ideas
Skill: Definition Question

7) An anecdote is

    A) a persuasive argument used to counteract the thesis statement.

    B) a brief entertaining story or illustration.

    C) a way of including expert testimony into the introduction.

    D) a fictional statement used to add humor to the speech introduction.

Answer: B
Page Ref: 216
Topic: Effective introductions
Skill: Definition Question

8) What is the purpose of the technique when a speaker makes reference to the introduction in the conclusion?

    A) providing a sense of closure   B) unnecessary repetition of material

    C) a good way to summarize the speech.   D) a way to build speaker credibility

Answer: A
Page Ref: 225-226
Topic: Effective conclusions
Skill: Definition Question

9) According to the authors, the most obvious purpose that you *must* accomplish in a speech introduction is
    A) to get the audience's attention.
    B) to introduce the topic of your speech.
    C) to establish your credibility.
    D) to establish proximity with your audience.

Answer: B
Page Ref: 213
Topic: Purposes of introductions
Skill: Description Question

10) In the introduction to your speech, a good way to establish your credibility is to
    A) start with a well known quotation.   B) be well prepared and confident.
    C) summarize your main ideas.   D) state your specific purpose.

Answer: B
Page Ref: 214
Topic: Purposes of introductions, establish your credibility
Skill: Description Question

11) A speaker who describes her or his main points as part of the introduction is utilizing what device?
    A) a credibility statement   B) a specific purpose statement
    C) a preview statement   D) an internal summary

Answer: C
Page Ref: 215
Topic: Purposes of introductions, preview your main ideas
Skill: Description Question

12) What must speakers remember when using humor in an introduction?
    A) Humor should only be used in a speech when the general purpose is to entertain.
    B) Humor should be used only if it is appropriate to the topic chosen.
    C) Humor in a speech is especially useful when the audience is linguistically diverse.
    D) Humor is best when it is general and overt since audiences don't generally understand irony.

Answer: B
Page Ref: 218-219
Topic: Effective introductions, humor
Skill: Description Question

13) In an introduction, you may ask a question that doesn't require a response but makes the audience think about your topic. This type of question is
   A) a rhetorical question.   B) an ambiguous question.
   C) a hypothetical question.   D) an unanswerable question.

Answer: A
Page Ref: 219
Topic: Effective introductions, questions
Skill: Description Question

14) Of the various types of speech introduction devices described in the text, which is generally delivered in an impromptu form?
   A) reference to a historical event   B) reference to a recent news event
   C) a personal reference   D) reference to the preceding speech

Answer: D
Page Ref: 222–223
Topic: Effective introductions, references to preceding speeches
Skill: Description Question

15) What should a speech conclusion do?
   A) Provide new material.   B) Summarize the main ideas.
   C) Stir guilt in the audience.   D) Fade out gradually.

Answer: B
Page Ref: 223
Topic: Purposes of conclusions
Skill: Description Question

16) Reemphasizing the central idea in a memorable way, moving an audience to action, and providing closure are all functions of
   A) the speech introduction.   B) the specific purpose.
   C) the central idea.   D) the speech conclusion.

Answer: D
Page Ref: 223
Topic: Purposes of conclusions
Skill: Description Question

17) Which of the following does the text state is an inherently interesting type of supporting material?
   A) a startling introductory device.   B) a specific purpose statement.
   C) a summary   D) an anecdote

Answer: D
Page Ref: 216
Topic: Effective introductions, illustrations or anecdotes
Skill: Example Question

18) A speech introduction that begins with, "Did you know that a light bulb has been invented that will last ten times as long as the ones we use today, but the government won't let it be marketed to the public?" is employing a device known as

    A) a startling statement.   B) a reference to a historical event.

    C) a personal reference.   D) an anecdote.

Answer: A
Page Ref: 217
Topic: Effective introductions, startling facts or statistics
Skill: Example Question

19) A speaker opens with the following question: "Can anyone tell me what edible item was said to be created on September 22, 1896 and then patented by December, 1903?" What device is being employed in this introduction?

    A) a preview of the topic   B) a startling fact or statistic

    C) a reference to a historical event   D) an effective use of humor

Answer: C
Page Ref: 220
Topic: Effective introductions, references to historical events
Skill: Example Question

20) Michael begins his speech: "Alex, Charley, Frances, Ivan, Jeanne, Karl, and Lisa. All are common names, but for the National Weather Service these names mean much more--these are names used for hurricanes tracked during the 2004 hurricane season." You recognize this type of introduction as

    A) a personal reference.   B) a reference to a recent event.

    C) a historical reference.   D) a startling statistic.

Answer: B
Page Ref: 220
Topic: Effective introductions, references to recent events
Skill: Example Question

21) Thanking someone for inviting you to speak, as part of your introduction, is termed

    A) a rhetorical device.   B) a reference to a recent event.

    C) a personal illustration.   D) a personal reference.

Answer: D
Page Ref: 221
Topic: Effective introductions, personal references
Skill: Example Question

22) The statement "This is great day, because so many people from so many walks of life have gathered in this place to celebrate the life of Martin Luther King, Jr." is an example of an introductory device called

   A) a reference to the occasion.   B) a reference to something personal.

   C) a reference to a recent event.   D) a reference to a historical event.

   Answer: A
   Page Ref: 221–222
   Topic: Effective introductions, references to the occasion
   Skill: Example Question

23) When Gloria said, "So we must all do something to end domestic violence; we must all be prepared to confront this issue in our own neighborhoods and homes, so that we become part of the solution, not part of the problem," you recognize this as

   A) a startling statement.

   B) a re-emphasis on the central idea.

   C) a statement to motivate the audience to respond.

   D) a concluding summary statement.

   Answer: C
   Page Ref: 224
   Topic: Purposes of conclusions
   Skill: Example Question

24) Terms like "finally," "in conclusion," and "in closing" are examples of

   A) devices to motivate an audience to respond or be moved to action.

   B) devices that provide closure for a speech.

   C) devices that summarize the main points in a speech.

   D) devices that reemphasize the main point in a memorable way.

   Answer: B
   Page Ref: 225
   Topic: Purposes of conclusions, provide closure
   Skill: Example Question

25) Dana opens her speech against abortion by putting up a transparency that shows a graphic image of an aborted fetus. Is this an effective opening?

   A) No; she should have opened with a verbal, rather that a visual attention getter.

   B) No; this type of graphic material may disgust and repel the audience.

   C) Yes; this was startling and vivid and got the audience's attention.

   D) Yes; an audience cannot ignore the truth when it is pointed out to them.

   Answer: B
   Page Ref: 213
   Topic: Purposes of introductions, get the audience's attention
   Skill: Application Question

26) In developing her speech on scuba diving, Rachael is trying to decide whether or not to tell the audience in her introduction that she has been a diver since she was Freshman in high school. She wonders if this will help or hurt her credibility. What textbook advice applies here?

   A) Rachael should avoid describing her experience with the topic because she will appear to be speaker centered and not audience centered.

   B) Rachael should give a brief, credibility-building explanation of her experience with the topic.

   C) Rachael should give a full explanation of her experiences with the topic, including when she started diving, how many years she's diving, how often she dives, etc.

   D) For the sake of suspense, Rachael should wait until her conclusion to describe her diving experience.

Answer: B
Page Ref: 214
Topic: Purposes of introductions, establish your credibility
Skill: Application Question

27) Janet's introduction contained the following remarks: "How many of you know someone who has tried to quit smoking, successfully or unsuccessfully? Have any of the smokers in this audience tried to quit? Well, if you have tried to quit and failed, you are among the 20 percent of Americans who have tried to quit multiple times. A few months ago I tried to quit, for the umpteenth time, but this time I made it. I'd like to tell you exactly how I made it." Which of the following statements is accurate about this introduction?

   A) Janet has too many devices in this introduction; the audience will be confused rather than intrigued by this introduction.

   B) Janet shouldn't discuss her own experience with quitting smoking because it sets up some distance between her and the audience.

   C) Janet has successfully combined introductory devices of questions to the audience, statistical information, and a personal reference.

   D) Janet has successfully combined introductory devices of startling statements, reference to historical events, and illustrations.

Answer: C
Page Ref: 219
Topic: Effective introductions, questions
Skill: Application Question

28) Leonard walked to the podium, made direct eye contact with the audience, then asked the audience: "Have you ever wondered what a hot dog is made of? Do you really want to know?" What introductory device was Leonard using?

   A) opening with a startling facts   B) asking rhetorical questions

   C) establishing his credibility   D) using personal references

Answer: B
Page Ref: 219
Topic: Effective introductions, questions
Skill: Application Question

29) In the speech just before Jerome's, the speaker covered some of the same material that Jerome was going to use in his speech on golf. Instead of letting this throw him, Jerome acknowledged the overlap in his introduction. Was this a wise thing to do, according to your text?

   A) No; drawing attention to the similarities in the two speeches was unnecessary and hurt Jerome's credibility.

   B) Yes; but only because Jerome made the point much more clearly and succinctly than the speaker before him.

   C) No; Jerome should not have mentioned the overlap because chances are the audience would not catch it.

   D) Yes; Jerome used an attention-getting, credibility-building device known as a reference to a preceding speech.

   Answer: D
   Page Ref: 222–223
   Topic: Effective introductions, references to preceding speeches
   Skill: Application Question

30) Meg has just finished her last main point, with its subpoints and supporting material. She concludes by saying "Finally..." then refers back to her introductory story. Does this describe an appropriate conclusion?

   A) Yes; Meg created a smooth bridge between her speech body and the conclusion.

   B) No; Meg forgot to add a summary of her points before concluding.

   C) No; Meg forgot to add a plea for action from her audience.

   D) Yes; Meg provided closure by tying the introduction and conclusion together.

   Answer: B
   Page Ref: 223
   Topic: Purposes of conclusions, summarize the speech
   Skill: Application Question

31) In her introduction to her speech about eating disorders, Sheila told the story of her friend who almost died of anorexia. In her conclusion, she reminded her audience of what her friend went through and explained that her friend was currently doing well in her battle against the disease. Was this an appropriate strategy for her speech?

   A) Yes; this is a concluding strategy known as a reference to the introduction.

   B) Yes; this is a concluding strategy known as a reference to the occasion.

   C) No; the introduction and conclusion are separate elements of a speech and should not overlap.

   D) Yes; this is a concluding strategy known as an appeal to action.

   Answer: A
   Page Ref: 226
   Topic: Effective conclusions, references to the introduction
   Skill: Application Question

32) In his speech about registering to vote, Dan explains the new legislation that allows voter registration to coincide with driver's license renewal. But he concludes the speech by stating that any person who is not registered should go by several locations that he has listed on the chalkboard and register in time for the next election. Finally, Dan reiterates: "Everyone please register to vote; it's your right and your duty as a citizen." What aspect of effective conclusions has Dan utilized?

    A) a personal reference to his own experience

    B) an inspirational appeal or challenge to the audience

    C) an appeal to action on the part of the audience

    D) an effective summary of main points in a speech

Answer: C
Page Ref: 228
Topic: Effective conclusions, appeals to action
Skill: Application Question

33) The first goal of the speech introduction is to gain the attention of the audience.

Answer: TRUE
Page Ref: 212
Topic: Purposes of introductions

34) The specific purpose is the first statement that a speaker should make to the audience.

Answer: FALSE
Page Ref: 213
Topic: Purposes of introductions

35) The impression an audience has of a speaker is termed prejudice.

Answer: FALSE
Page Ref: 214
Topic: Purposes of introductions

36) Proximity is the idea that the information being presented in the speech affects the audience directly.

Answer: TRUE
Page Ref: 214
Topic: Purposes of introductions

37) The main way of building credibility with an audience is by using personal experiences in the speech.

Answer: FALSE
Page Ref: 214
Topic: Purposes of introductions

38) One of the purposes of a conclusion is to help your audience remember your main ideas.

Answer: TRUE
Page Ref: 223
Topic: Purposes of conclusions

39) Any of the methods used for the introduction of your speech can be used in the conclusion.

Answer: TRUE
Page Ref: 225
Topic: Effective conclusions

40) Providing closure in a conclusion lets the audience know that the speech is finished.

Answer: TRUE
Page Ref: 225
Topic: Purposes of conclusions

41) You can attain closure both verbally and nonverbally in a speech.

Answer: TRUE
Page Ref: 225
Topic: Purposes of conclusions, provide closure

42) In a persuasive speech, it is effective to make a final plea for action and tell your audience specifically how they can act.

Answer: TRUE
Page Ref: 228
Topic: Effective conclusions

43) Five purposes of speech introductions are explored in your text. Identify and briefly explain all of these five purposes.

Page Ref: 212–213
Topic: Purposes of introductions

44) What is a rhetorical question? Explain what it is, how it can be presented, and why it is effective in getting the audience's attention.

Answer: no answer
Page Ref: 219
Topic: Effective introductions

45) Give an example of each of the following introductory devices: (1) references to historical events; (2) references to recent events; (3) personal references; (4) references to the occasion; and (5) references to preceding speeches.

Page Ref: 220–222
Topic: Effective introductions

46) Four purposes of speech conclusions are explored in your text. Give examples of three of these in a topic of your choosing.

Page Ref: 223–225
Topic: Purposes of conclusions

47) Describe two verbal and two nonverbal means of providing closure in a speech conclusion.

Page Ref: 225
Topic: Purposes of conclusions

48) Your textbook provides five functions of the speech introduction. In a thorough essay, identify these functions and explain their importance to a public speech.

Page Ref: 212–215
Topic: Purposes of introductions

49) Using the hypothetical speech topic, "The Importance of an Internship," develop four possible introductions to this speech, illustrating your understanding of the various devices that can be used in an introduction.

Page Ref: 216–223
Topic: Effective introductions

50) Using the hypothetical speech topic, "Human Cloning," develop three possible conclusions for this speech, illustrating your understanding of devices that make for effective conclusions.

Page Ref: 225–228
Topic: Effective conclusions

Chapter 11 Outlining and Editing Your Speech

1) Just as a traveler needs a map for a journey, a speaker needs a map for a speech. This detailed map of a speech is

A) an audience analysis.   B) a preparation outline.

C) a delivery outline.   D) a bibliography.

Answer: B
Page Ref: 234
Topic: Developing your preparation outline
Skill: Definition Question

2) Writing down your main ideas, subpoints, and supporting material, then using geometric shapes and arrows to indicate logical relationships is a technique known as

A) brainstorming.   B) laddering.   C) mapping.   D) graphing.

Answer: C
Page Ref: 235
Topic: Developing your preparation outline
Skill: Definition Question

3) Conventional use of numbered and lettered heading and subheadings to indicate the relationships among parts of the speech is known as a

A) proportioned outline.   B) standard outline form.

C) clustering of ideas.   D) key word outline.

Answer: B
Page Ref: 236
Topic: Developing your preparation outline
Skill: Definition Question

4) The speaker's outline which contains the specific purpose, the introduction, all main ideas with supporting material, and a conclusion is

A) the numerical outline.   B) the delivery outline.

C) the preparation outline.   D) the preliminary outline.

Answer: C
Page Ref: 235
Topic: Developing your preparation outline
Skill: Definition Question

5) In an outline, Roman numerals are used to indicate

A) the main ideas.   B) the subpoints.

C) the introduction.   D) the conclusion.

Answer: A
Page Ref: 236
Topic: Developing your preparation outline
Skill: Definition Question

6) When using indentation in an outline, indent to

    A) the letter or Roman numeral of the point above.

    B) the first word under the point above.

    C) the margin of the page as formatted.

    D) one space past the first word under the point above.

Answer: B
Page Ref: 236
Topic: Developing your preparation outline
Skill: Definition Question

7) Before presenting your speech in front of a full audience you practice and discover that your speech is too long. What should be done?

    A) Change to a topic that is not as detailed in order to fit the time limit.

    B) Edit the speech by reviewing the specific purpose--you may be trying to accomplish too much in the speech

    C) Limit the number of visual aids because they add to the length of the presentation.

    D) Stick to the ideas that you believe are most important; the audience can do additional research on the topic after the speech.

Answer: B
Page Ref: 240-241
Topic: Editing your speech
Skill: Definition Question

8) The delivery outline is

    A) the same as the preparation outline.

    B) the same as the preparation outline, but with the citations written in.

    C) the preparation enlarged and double-spaced.

    D) much shorter than the preparation outline and tailored to the individual speaker.

Answer: D
Page Ref: 242-243
Topic: Developing your delivery outline and speaking notes
Skill: Definition Question

9) According to the text, what is the purpose of using complete sentences in a preparation outline?

    A) You will use these exact same sentences when you deliver the speech.

    B) This will ensure that you use the best wording possible for the speech.

    C) This will help you judge the coherence of the speech.

    D) This will help you to realize the importance of good grammar.

Answer: C
Page Ref: 235
Topic: Developing your preparation outline
Skill: Description Question

10) What does your textbook state is the major benefit of using standard outline form?

   A) It helps you to remember your topic.

   B) It points out possible phrases to help you remember.

   C) It helps you remember the main ideas of your speech.

   D) It points out relationships between ideas and supporting material.

Answer: D
Page Ref: 236
Topic: Developing your preparation outline
Skill: Description Question

11) What is one of the features of the standard outline form?

   A) Use at least two subdivisions, if any, for each point.

   B) Use Arabic numbers for all your subpoints.

   C) Indent to the number or letter above.

   D) Use capital letters for all subpoints.

Answer: A
Page Ref: 236
Topic: Developing your preparation outline
Skill: Description Question

12) The preparation outline should contain everything but

   A) transitions and signposts.   B) directions for delivering your speech.

   C) your specific purpose and a blueprint.   D) your main ideas and all support.

Answer: B
Page Ref: 236
Topic: Developing your preparation outline
Skill: Description Question

13) When should a speaker edit their speech?

   A) When the audience begins to applaud when the speaker says, "In conclusion..."

   B) As the speaker is practicing from the preparation outline and discovers there is too much information.

   C) During the speech when the audience is not responding to the visual aids.

   D) Once it is in preparation outline form it needs no further editing.

Answer: B
Page Ref: 240
Topic: Editing your speech
Skill: Description Question

14) The delivery outline

    A) should be written in complete sentences.

    B) should have the specific purpose at the top.

    C) should be brief and have speaking notes.

    D) should have every transition written out.

Answer: C
Page Ref: 242-243
Topic: Developing your delivery outline and speaking notes
Skill: Description Question

15) When you finally deliver your speech, you should speak from

    A) the bibliographic outline.   B) the preparation outline.

    C) the delivery outline.   D) the written out speech.

Answer: C
Page Ref: 242-243
Topic: Developing your delivery outline and speaking notes
Skill: Description Question

16) What tip does your textbook suggest regarding the use of speaking notes?

    A) Type or print information so that it can be easily read.

    B) Include your written out introduction and conclusion.

    C) Do not write out statistics or direct quotations.

    D) Use complete sentences throughout your notes.

Answer: A
Page Ref: 246
Topic: Developing your delivery outline and speaking notes
Skill: Description Question

17) Gina shows her preparation outline to a classmate, Fran, who says that Gina has done it wrong because she used complete sentences instead of key phrases or single words. Who's right?

    A) Gina, because a preparation outline should be drafted in complete sentences.

    B) Fran, because the very nature of outlining calls for key phrases, not complete statements.

    C) Fran, because Gina confused the format for the preparation outline with the delivery outline.

    D) Both women are right; the preparation outline can be written in a number of ways.

Answer: A
Page Ref: 235
Topic: Developing your preparation outline
Skill: Example Question

18) Why would the following be an incomplete example of a preparation outline?
   I. The status of our nation's blood supply has always been a problem.
      A. The current status of our blood supply creates a bleak picture.
         1. There is a deletion of blood bank supplies.

   A) There is only one subdivision used.

   B) The subpoint in the outline does not follow correct indentation standards.

   C) The subpoint in the outline is not logically divided.

   D) Only Roman numerals should appear in outlines, not Arabic numbers.

   Answer: A
   Page Ref: 235–236
   Topic: Developing your preparation outline
   Skill: Example Question

19) Why would the following be an example of an incomplete standard outlining form?

   I. Current local efforts to recycle common household products are
      increasingly successful.
      A. More community involvement
         1. Each day more types of items are added to the list of what can be
            recycled.
         2. People are becoming more aware of local recycling centers.

   A) The main idea is not a complete sentence.

   B) The subpoints in the outline do not follow correct indentation standards.

   C) The subpoints in the outline are not logically divided.

   D) The subpoint is not written out as a complete sentence.

   Answer: D
   Page Ref: 236
   Topic: Developing your preparation outline
   Skill: Example Question

20) What aspect of standard outlining procedure is <u>violated</u> in the following example?

   I. The Rocky Mountains were formed in stages, over a long period of time.
      1. Mountains are affected by geographic and environmental events.
      2. Mountains provide a sort of "blueprint" as to what has occurred in a
         certain region.
   II. The Rockies are younger mountains than the Swiss Alps.

   A) numbering/lettering   B) subordination
   C) indentation   D) logical division

   Answer: A
   Page Ref: 236
   Topic: Developing your preparation outline
   Skill: Example Question

21) Sally created a preparation outline and included main ideas, as well as numerous subdivisions and subpoints. She also included the specific purpose at the top of her outline. According to the text, why is her outline incomplete?

A) she placed the specific purpose in the wrong location as it should be included inside of the outline.

B) she used too many subdivisions to create a logical argument.

C) she did not include an introduction, blueprint, key signposts or a conclusion to her outline.

D) she did not include a summary that explained why she chose the topic she did.

Answer: C
Page Ref: 236–237
Topic: Developing your preparation outline
Skill: Example Question

22) In rehearsing her speech, Lesa used phrases such as, "In my opinion," "When all is said and done," and "I'd like to offer several examples to support my position." Erin said that Lesa should eliminate these phrases. Is Erin right?

A) Yes; they are trite and overused sayings anyway.

B) Yes; speakers should eliminate phrases that add no meaning to the message.

C) No, these are legitimate transitional phrases that Lesa could use in her speech.

D) No, because Lesa has prepared this speech and is comfortable with the content.

Answer: B
Page Ref: 241–242
Topic: Editing your speech
Skill: Example Question

23) George shows Laura his delivery outline for an upcoming speech. She criticizes George for including supporting material and signposts in his outline. Who is right?

A) Laura is right because supporting material and signposts do not belong in a delivery outline.

B) George is right because all elements of a speech should be detailed in the delivery outline.

C) George is right because supporting material and signposts should be included in a delivery outline.

D) Laura is right about the supporting material, but George is right about the signposts.

Answer: C
Page Ref: 242–243
Topic: Developing your delivery outline and speaking notes
Skill: Example Question

24) Marissa's speaking notes were filled with drawings, words, and symbols. Is this a fine method for creating speaking notes?

    A) No; the speaking cards should be in outline form and have no pictures.

    B) Yes; it is fine to prepare your notes in any form as long as they make sense to you.

    C) No, because notes of this kind generally distract rather than help speakers.

    D) Yes, but it is only okay to use drawings and symbols at the beginning and end of the speech where they will not get in the way of the topic.

Answer: B
Page Ref: 247
Topic: Developing your delivery outline and speaking notes
Skill: Example Question

25) A general rule of thumb when estimating the time frame for your introduction and conclusion is to remember that:

    A) the introduction should be 10 minutes long and the conclusion should be five minutes.

    B) the conclusion is generally more important than the introduction and this should be represented in the time allotment for each part.

    C) the introduction and the conclusion should each represent 10 percent of your speaking time.

    D) the introduction is generally more important than the conclusion and this should be represented in the time allotment for each part.

Answer: C
Page Ref: 242
Topic: Editing your speech
Skill: Application Question

26) What is <u>wrong</u> in the following segment of a speech preparation outline?

    I. Romantic relationships rarely develop like they are portrayed in Hollywood movies.
    A. Many times, movies show "opposites who attract," when in real life "similars" attract.
    B. Movies tend to over-dramatize conflicts, when actually subtle conflicts are more the norm.
    II. Successful romantic relationships take time and effort.

    A) The outline does not use the standard outline indentation.

    B) Roman numerals correctly appear in the outline.

    C) Each point is expressed in a complete sentence.

    D) The subpoints should be capital letters.

Answer: A
Page Ref: 236
Topic: Developing your preparation outline
Skill: Application Question

27) Stuart has always been a nervous public speaker, but this time he's going to prepare an outline that will really help him calm his nerves and build his confidence. He's going to completely write out his introduction and conclusion and include them on his delivery outline. Is this advisable, according to your textbook?

   A) Yes; anything a speaker can do to reduce nervousness is advisable.

   B) Yes; full statements and explanations are central aspects of the delivery outline.

   C) No; he should only write the first sentence of the intro and final sentence of the conclusion, if needed.

   D) No; if he writes out the intro and conclusion, he should write out everything on the outline.

   Answer: C
   Page Ref: 242-243
   Topic: Developing your delivery outline and speaking notes
   Skill: Application Question

28) Susanne wrote her preparation outline but decided that it contained too much material. She went back to her speech and thought about who her audience would be. She then cut two of her main points out of her speech. Was this a good way to minimize her information?

   A) No; Suzanne needed to include all major points on her preparation outline.

   B) Yes; Suzanne was considering her audience. She removed two points because she decided her audience did not need to know this information.

   C) No; Suzanne should have focused on removing any extra words to cut down the information, even though her extra points were not crucial to her audience.

   D) No; Suzanne should not have to cut any of her material.

   Answer: B
   Page Ref: 240-241
   Topic: Editing your speech
   Skill: Application Question

29) Bernard is rehearsing a class demonstration speech that he has to present in two days. As he rehearses from his delivery outline, he continues to revise the outline. He changes the order of some points, deletes some extraneous detail, and reworks his conclusion. According to your textbook, is this kind of revision advisable?

   A) No; Bernard is revising too much and too close to the presentation date.

   B) Yes, with regard for the ordering and deletions, but you should never alter your conclusion.

   C) Yes; this kind of revising of the delivery outline is expected and helpful during rehearsal.

   D) No; once the delivery outline is written, it should be rehearsed as is with no changes.

   Answer: C
   Page Ref: 242-243
   Topic: Developing your delivery outline and speaking notes
   Skill: Application Question

30) Sandy decided that she needed almost all of her material on her delivery outline because she had so many statistics and direct quotations. She liked to use note cards so that she could move from the podium but was distressed to find she had fifteen note cards. When delivering the speech, she dropped her cards and couldn't find her place. What does your text suggest to help a speaker avoid a situation like this?

    A) Don't include so many statistics on your delivery outline.

    B) Don't include quotations, or if you do, don't cite the source.

    C) Don't make a delivery outline like this; just memorize the speech.

    D) Don't have too many cards, if possible; always be sure and number them.

Answer: D
Page Ref: 246-247
Topic: Speaking notes
Skill: Application Question

31) Maria had worked on her preparation outline for a long time and is satisfied with it. She practices several times from it, and then transfers her speaking outline onto note cards. She decides to put her introduction on one card, each main idea on a separate card, her conclusion on another card. Each card is a different color. Is this a good idea?

    A) No, because this is too much information for a delivery outline.

    B) No, because colored cards will distract the audience from her message.

    C) Yes, because delivery notes are personal and can be any format.

    D) Yes, because according to the text, each main idea should be on a separate card.

Answer: C
Page Ref: 246-249
Topic: Developing your delivery outline and speaking notes
Skill: Application Question

32) On the evaluations for your previous two speeches, you received a comment about a "speedy vocal delivery." You want to make sure not to repeat that mistake on your next speaking assignment, so you write in the margins of your note cards "Slow down." Is this proper for speaking notes?

    A) Yes, but only if you include those comments on your original preparation outline.

    B) No; comments like this will only make you more nervous when you speak.

    C) Yes; comments like this are effective delivery reminders on speaking notes.

    D) No; comments like this can be seen by the audience, and you will lose credibility.

Answer: C
Page Ref: 246
Topic: Speaking notes
Skill: Application Question

33) The preparation outline can be viewed as a map of your speech.

Answer: TRUE
Page Ref: 235
Topic: Developing your preparation outline

34) Mapping and clustering are used mainly when the speaker has a mental block on a topic.

Answer: FALSE
Page Ref: 235
Topic: Developing your preparation outline

35) A preparation outline will help you to determine the content you would like to cover as well as alert you if the speech is too long.

Answer: TRUE
Page Ref: 240
Topic: Editing your speech

36) If you have subpoint A in your preparation outline, you must have subpoint B as well.

Answer: TRUE
Page Ref: 236
Topic: Developing your preparation outline

37) If signposts are lacking in your preparation outline, the speech will lack coherence.

Answer: TRUE
Page Ref: 237
Topic: Developing your preparation outline

38) When editing the speech you must review the specific purpose, consider the audience, and make sure the ideas are simply stated.

Answer: TRUE
Page Ref: 240
Topic: Editing your speech

39) The delivery outline should include transitions, citings, and directions for delivery.

Answer: TRUE
Page Ref: 242–243
Topic: Developing your delivery outline and speaking notes

40) The specific purpose must be written and labeled at the top of the delivery outline.

Answer: FALSE
Page Ref: 242
Topic: Preparation outline, delivery outline

41) As you rehearse your speech, you will find that you will need your preparation outline more than a delivery outline.

Answer: FALSE
Page Ref: 242
Topic: Preparation outline, delivery outline

42) Note cards are always preferable to full sheets of paper because they are less conspicuous to an audience.

Answer: FALSE
Page Ref: 246
Topic: Developing your delivery outline and speaking notes

43) Discuss briefly three ways that a preparation outline differs from a delivery outline.
Page Ref: 235–240, 242–245
Topic: Preparation outline, delivery outline

44) Explain the principle of subdivision within standard outline form.
Page Ref: 236
Topic: Developing your preparation outline

45) Explain the use of Roman numerals, capital letters, Arabic numbers, and small letters in a standard outline form.
Page Ref: 236
Topic: Developing your preparation outline

46) Briefly explain what is necessary in editing a speech that is too long.
Page Ref: 240–242
Topic: Editing your speech

47) What is the purpose of adding speaking notes to a delivery outline?
Page Ref: 246–248
Topic: Developing your delivery outline and speaking notes

48) Explain in detail how to develop and construct a preparation outline.
Page Ref: 235–237
Topic: Developing your preparation outline

49) Imagine that you will be presenting an informative speech on this topic: "Commercials I Have Learned to Love." Develop a preparation outline for this topic which demonstrates your understanding of correct outline form. Include a purpose statement, central idea, introduction, main points, subpoints, and a conclusion in the outline.
Page Ref: 235–239
Topic: Developing your preparation outline

50) What steps are necessary in developing a delivery outline? In a well–developed essay, discuss each step and the value and use of each.
Page Ref: 242–245
Topic: Developing your delivery outline and speaking notes

Chapter 12 Using Words Well: Speaker Language and Style

1) Oral language is different from written language in that it

    A) is more formal and precise.   B) allows for few repetitions.

    C) is more personal and simple.   D) uses few figures of speech.

Answer: C
Page Ref: 255
Topic: Oral versus written language style
Skill: Definition Question

2) A word that is specific and appeals to at least one of our five senses is known as

    A) an abstract word.   B) a concrete word.

    C) a sensual word.   D) a simple word.

Answer: B
Page Ref: 256–257
Topic: Using words effectively
Skill: Definition Question

3) A cliche is

    A) a dictionary definition of a word.

    B) used within a speech to present specific information.

    C) an overused expression that may make listeners tune out.

    D) a concrete word or phrase which expresses clear communication.

Answer: C
Page Ref: 257
Topic: Using words effectively
Skill: Definition Question

4) The term that applies to the meaning of a word based on our past experiences is

    A) connotation.   B) denotation.   C) imagination.   D) colloquialism.

Answer: A
Page Ref: 258
Topic: Using words effectively
Skill: Definition Question

5) The literal or dictionary meaning of a word is

    A) connotation.   B) denotation.   C) regionalism.   D) vernacular.

Answer: B
Page Ref: 258
Topic: Using words effectively
Skill: Definition Question

6) A variety of English that includes words or phrases used by a specific ethnic group is called

    A) regionalisms.   B) ethnic vernacular.

    C) connotation.   D) jargon.

Answer: B
Page Ref: 259
Topic: Adapting your language style to diverse learners
Skill: Definition Question

7) Words that are particular to a profession are known as

    A) jargon.   B) vernacular.   C) sexist.   D) regional.

Answer: A
Page Ref: 259
Topic: Adapting your language style to diverse learners
Skill: Definition Question

8) Language used by speakers during momentous or overwhelming times is known as

    A) specialized jargon.   B) crisis rhetoric.

    C) personification.   D) vernacular.

Answer: B
Page Ref: 262
Topic: Creating figurative images
Skill: Definition Question

9) Antithesis is defined as

    A) going against the thesis that was established within the introduction.

    B) having two or more clauses or sentences with the same grammatical pattern.

    C) a sentence having a parallel structure, but with the two parts contrasting each other in meaning.

    D) closing a series of ideas that are strikingly less important than what has preceded it.

Answer: C
Page Ref: 264
Topic: Creating cadence
Skill: Definition Question

10) The most important difference between oral language and written language is

    A) written language uses ordinary words, commonly understood.

    B) oral language uses few personal pronouns such as "you."

    C) written language is less formal and more repetitious.

    D) oral language allows for interaction with the audience.

Answer: D
Page Ref: 255
Topic: Oral versus written language style
Skill: Description Question

11) An alphabetical list of words and their synonyms is a:

   A) word bank.   B) dictionary.   C) a thesaurus   D) encyclopedia.

Answer: C
Page Ref: 257
Topic: Using words effectively
Skill: Description Question

12) To "use appropriate language" in a speech implies

   A) avoiding any words not found in a dictionary of U. S. Standard English.

   B) avoiding language that will offend people of different cultures, races, sexes, or other subgroups.

   C) avoiding language that may be too dramatic or colorful for your audience.

   D) avoiding language that is too informal and uses sentences that are too short and choppy.

Answer: B
Page Ref: 259-260
Topic: Adapting your language style to diverse learners
Skill: Description Question

13) When speakers substitutes the word "flight attendant" for "stewardess" or "steward, " they are using language that is

   A) politically incorrect.   B) biased.

   C) non-sexist.   D) standard.

Answer: C
Page Ref: 260-261
Topic: Adapting language style, use unbiased language
Skill: Description Question

14) When a speaker compares an abstract idea to a concrete image, she or he is using the figure of speech known as

   A) an inversion.   B) a metaphor.   C) parallelism.   D) personification.

Answer: B
Page Ref: 262
Topic: Crafting memorable word structures
Skill: Description Question

15) When you keep your audience in suspense or say something in your speech that is different from the expected, you are

   A) creating cadence.   B) creating confusion.

   C) creating a sense of drama. D) creating memorable imagery.

Answer: C
Page Ref: 262-263
Topic: Creating drama
Skill: Description Question

16) One strategy in improving your speaking style by creating cadence is

    A) to leave out a word the audience expects.

    B) reverse the normal word order in sentences.

    C) use words with strong audience connotation.

    D) to use parallelism in sentences or phrases.

Answer: D
Page Ref: 263–264
Topic: Crafting memorable word structures, creating cadence
Skill: Description Question

17) If you interpret the statement, "that's one <u>bad</u> car" as a positive, complimentary description, you are using

    A) a connotative meaning of the word "bad."

    B) a denotative meaning of the word "bad."

    C) a form of discriminatory language.

    D) a form of jargonal language.

Answer: A
Page Ref: 258
Topic: Using words effectively
Skill: Example Question

18) What is wrong with the following statement in a speech? "If you believe we should have stiffer penalties for juvenile offenders, then write your congressman."

    A) The language is controversial and likely to incite a negative emotional response in listeners.

    B) The language is sexist, as the term "congressman" implies only men serve in the legislature.

    C) The language should be more vivid and specific in order to move the audience to action.

    D) The language should create a sense of drama and suspense in order to move the audience.

Answer: B
Page Ref: 260–261
Topic: Adapting your language style to diverse learners
Skill: Example Question

19) Statements such as, "Money talks," "That's my car; isn't she beautiful," and "The wind moaned and screeched," are all examples of

    A) personification.   B) personalism.   C) metaphors.   D) similes.

Answer: A
Page Ref: 262
Topic: Creating figurative images
Skill: Example Question

20) President Lincoln declared, in his first inaugural address, "I am loath to close. We are not enemies, but friends. We must not be enemies." Which language device for good speaking was he using?

    A) He was using the device of a literary metaphor.

    B) He was creating drama by building suspense.

    C) He was using short, choppy sentences to add impact.

    D) He was creating cadence through alliteration.

Answer: C
Page Ref: 262–263
Topic: Creating drama
Skill: Example Question

21) President George W. Bush, in eulogizing President Reagan, stated when Ronald Reagan was a child he "knew the world as a place of open plains, quiet streets, gas–lit rooms, and carriages drawn by horse." Which language device was President Bush using when he said "carriages drawn by horses"?

    A) He was using antithesis.   B) He was using metaphor.

    C) He was using inversion.   D) He was using personification.

Answer: C
Page Ref: 263
Topic: Using words effectively
Skill: Example Question

22) Using a key word or phrase at the end rather than the beginning of a sentence, such as in the statement "She's an inspiration, a best friend, and a teacher; she's also my mom" is a stylistic device known as

    A) alliteration.   B) omission.   C) suspension.   D) inversion.

Answer: C
Page Ref: 263
Topic: Crafting memorable word structures
Skill: Example Question

23) When Reverend Jesse Jackson says, "We must relate instead of debate; we must inspire instead of retire; and we must repair instead of despair," what linguistic device is he using?

    A) metaphor   B) omission   C) parallelism   D) inversion

Answer: C
Page Ref: 264
Topic: Crafting memorable word structures
Skill: Example Question

24) The statement, "Now is the time for determination, decisiveness, and dedication" employs what linguistic device?

   A) antithesis   B) alliteration   C) repetition   D) parallelism

Answer: B
Page Ref: 265–266
Topic: Crafting memorable word structures, creating cadence
Skill: Example Question

25) As an introduction to a term paper, Louis wrote the following: "It is a pervasive fact that poverty exists, in fact, it is on the rampage in this country. How can the average, concerned citizen do her or his part to counteract this societal problem that is spiraling out of control?" What would Louis have to do to change his written style into an oral style, so that this introduction would work for a speech?

   A) He would need to reword his biased, stereotypical language.

   B) He would need to use more personal, less formal language.

   C) He would need to use more abstractions, rather than concrete terms.

   D) He would need to reduce the amount of repetition in his written style.

Answer: B
Page Ref: 255
Topic: Oral versus written language style
Skill: Application Question

26) In Jillian's persuasive speech, on why school teachers deserve a pay raise, she used the following phrases: "raises have been few and far between," "faculty must rob Peter to pay Paul," "faculty just want a fair shake," and "the administration must demonstrate a sense of fair play." These statements are all examples of

   A) jargon   B) regionalisms   C) cliches   D) cadence

Answer: C
Page Ref: 257
Topic: Using words effectively
Skill: Application Question

27) When Kenny was speaking, he said, "That car was hot!" Some of the members of the audience thought Kenny meant it was a really nice looking car, others thought he meant it was a stolen vehicle, while a few others just thought he was talking about the temperature of the car. What Kenny meant by that statement was that he thought it was a really nice car. What was happening here?

    A) Kenny inappropriately used abstract words when he should have used more concrete ones.

    B) The audience used a connotative meaning for "hot," when Kenny intended a denotative meaning.

    C) Kenny should have used a more complex word for "hot," so that the audience would understand.

    D) The audience used a denotative meaning for "hot," when Kenny intended to establish personification.

Answer: A
Page Ref: 256–257
Topic: Using words effectively
Skill: Application Question

28) Adriana presented a moving speech about the increase of random violence in her hometown. She cited an incident in which a male nurse rushed to the aid of a car crash victim and was inexplicably shot and killed by this victim. From this brief description, did the speaker use appropriate language in the speech?

    A) Yes; she used vivid, simple language that listeners could understand.

    B) No; she used technical jargon without defining what she meant.

    C) Yes; she used concrete language, but in an interesting, engaging way.

    D) No; she used a biased form of language when she said "male nurse."

Answer: D
Page Ref: 260–261
Topic: Adapting your language style to diverse learners
Skill: Application Question

29) Jill's speech was successful on many counts, one being an effective use of language. She used colorful words and imagery to get her audience thinking about her topic. She wanted them to think about it, possibly change their views of it, and then go out and do something about it. Which guideline about language usage offered in your text is reflected in this example?

    A) Use unbiased words.   B) Use abstract words.

    C) Use simple words.   D) Use vivid words.

Answer: D
Page Ref: 261–262
Topic: Crafting memorable word structures
Skill: Application Question

30) In his speech about the Titanic, Keifer said the following: "She was the new world, the new technology, the best of the best. But a technology that failed, leaving many souls in a cold, watery grave." What form of effective language usage has Keifer employed?

   A) omission   B) simile   C) metaphor   D) alliteration

Answer: C
Page Ref: 262
Topic: Creating figurative images
Skill: Application Question

31) In a speech about preparing oneself for the death of a loved one, Amber made repeated reference to "Death, the unwanted stranger at the door." She hoped to create a sense of drama for her audience, while at the same time getting them to seriously consider her points. What figure of speech did Amber use in her presentation?

   A) metaphor   B) simile   C) hyperbole   D) personification

Answer: D
Page Ref: 262
Topic: Creating figurative images
Skill: Application Question

32) To add a sort of poetic touch to his speech on inspirational teachers, Julian described his favorite high school teacher as "an inspiration unequaled," "a genius unrivaled," and "a comedian unbridled." What stylistic, dramatic device did Julian employ?

   A) omission   B) inversion   C) suspension   D) antithesis

Answer: B
Page Ref: 263
Topic: Crafting memorable word structures
Skill: Application Question

33) Newspaper headlines such as, "Include your children when baking cookies," and "Miners refuse to work after death," are illustrations of effective, clear, and accurate attention –grabbers.

Answer: FALSE
Page Ref: 254
Topic: Using words well: speaker language and style

34) Written communication often uses less formal language and structure compared to spoken communication.

Answer: FALSE
Page Ref: 255
Topic: Oral versus written language style

35) It is a good idea to check a thesaurus when searching for a specific, concrete word.

Answer: TRUE
Page Ref: 257
Topic: Using words effectively

36) Connotation is the literal, or dictionary definition, of a word.

Answer: FALSE
Page Ref: 258
Topic: Using words effectively

37) A variety of English that includes words and phrases used by a specific ethnic group is called regionalisms.

Answer: FALSE
Page Ref: 259
Topic: Adapting your language style to diverse learners

38) A simile is a figure of speech which implies a comparison using "like" or "as."

Answer: TRUE
Page Ref: 262
Topic: Creating figurative images

39) Using language that keeps your audience in suspense or catches them off guard are ways of creating drama in a speech.

Answer: TRUE
Page Ref: 262-263
Topic: Crafting memorable word structures

40) The best way to create cadence in a speech is to use rhyming words.

Answer: FALSE
Page Ref: 263-264
Topic: Crafting memorable word structures, creating cadence

41) When Winston Churchill used the phrase, "virility, valour, and civic virtue" in his speech, he was using alliteration.

Answer: TRUE
Page Ref: 265-266
Topic: Crafting memorable word structures, creating cadence

42) Including highly stylized language can put the focus on your speech content rather than on language itself.

Answer: FALSE
Page Ref: 267-268
Topic: Tips for using language effectively

43) Explain how written language and oral language are different.
Page Ref: 255-256
Topic: Oral versus written language style

44) Define denotation and connotation and tell how they differ. Give an original example of each.

Page Ref: 258
Topic: Using words effectively

45) Define the following words and tell how each might be best reflected in a speech: simile, metaphor, personification.

Page Ref: 262
Topic: Crafting memorable word structures

46) Briefly describe how cadence is created when using parallelism, antithesis, repetition, and alliteration. Give an example of each.

Page Ref: 263–266
Topic: Crafting memorable word structures, creating cadence

47) The text offered four tips for using language effectively. Briefly describe these four ideas here.

Page Ref: 267–268
Topic: Tips for using language effectively

48) Contrast the oral style of language with the written style, making reference to the three factors explained in your text. Make sure to relate your information to the public speaking context.

Page Ref: 255–256
Topic: Oral versus written language style

49) Your textbook describes three factors for using words effectively in a public speech. In a thorough essay, first identify and define these three factors. Then, using the hypothetical speech topic, "The Best Movie Ever Made," provide an example of language used in the speech for each factor.

Page Ref: 256–259
Topic: Using words effectively

50) With the use of language, a public speaker can create drama and cadence in a speech. First explain how these two devices can add power and memorability to your speech. Then, choose two methods your textbook suggests for creating drama and two for creating cadence. Explain each method and offer a brief example for each.

Page Ref: 261–267
Topic: Crafting memorable word structures

Chapter 13 Delivering Your Speech

1) When it comes to public speaking, people have certain expectations as to how you should communicate. This represents the
   A) verbal expectancy theory.
   B) communication delivery theory.
   C) nonverbal expectancy theory.
   D) standard delivery style theory.

   Answer: C
   Page Ref: 275
   Topic: The power of speech delivery
   Skill: Definition Question

2) In a public speaking situation, the speaker should pay attention to how emotions are communicated when delivering a speech because the emotions could be catchy. This represents the
   A) emotional contagion theory.
   B) nonverbal expectancy theory.
   C) communication delivery theory.
   D) verbal expectancy theory.

   Answer: A
   Page Ref: 276
   Topic: The power of speech delivery
   Skill: Definition Question

3) Delivering a speech in a conversational style from a well-developed and researched outline is termed
   A) memorized delivery.
   B) manuscript delivery.
   C) extemporaneous delivery.
   D) impromptu delivery.

   Answer: C
   Page Ref: 279
   Topic: Methods of delivery
   Skill: Definition Question

4) Without uttering a word, an audience can be quieted by holding up the palm of your hand to calm a noisy crowd. This is the nonverbal function of
   A) repeating.
   B) contradicting.
   C) substituting.
   D) complementing.

   Answer: C
   Page Ref: 283
   Topic: Characteristics of effective delivery
   Skill: Definition Question

5) Behaviors such as eye contact, appropriate gestures, and physical closeness that enhance the quality of the relationship between the speaker and listeners is known as

A) nonverbal behaviors.   B) immediacy behaviors.

C) delivery behaviors.   D) concurrence behaviors.

Answer: B
Page Ref: 285
Topic: Characteristics of effective delivery, movement
Skill: Definition Question

6) A consistent style of pronouncing words that is common to an ethnic group or geographic region is

A) vocal variation.   B) articulation.

C) dialect.   D) intonation patterns.

Answer: C
Page Ref: 287–288
Topic: Vocal delivery
Skill: Definition Question

7) An attitude that one's own cultural approaches are superior to those of other cultures is termed

A) ethnocentrism.   B) ethnic racism.   C) discrimination.   D) homophobia.

Answer: A
Page Ref: 293
Topic: Audience diversity and delivery
Skill: Definition Question

8) Sometimes listeners may ask questions at the end of your speech that are unrelated to your talk. By finding a way to gently guide your questioners back to the message you are

A) paraphrasing their question.   B) listening non-judgmentally.

C) staying on message.   D) neutralizing hostile questions.

Answer: C
Page Ref: 299
Topic: Responding to questions
Skill: Definition Question

9) What is most important when a speaker is communicating emotional feelings, attitudes, likes, and dislikes to an audience?

A) verbal communication   B) nonverbal communication

C) good eye contact   D) clear articulation

Answer: B
Page Ref: 275
Topic: The power of speech delivery
Skill: Description Question

10) When the President of the U.S. delivers his State of the Union speech, what method of delivery will he use?

    A) memorized.   B) extemporaneous.

    C) manuscript.   D) impromptu.

Answer: C
Page Ref: 276
Topic: Methods of delivery
Skill: Description Question

11) When asked to deliver a speech at the last moment, the type of delivery style you will use is

    A) extemporaneous.   B) manuscript.

    C) impromptu.   D) memorized.

Answer: C
Page Ref: 277-278
Topic: Methods of delivery
Skill: Description Question

12) The ability to monitor your audience's response and adjust your message accordingly is a benefit of

    A) good facial expression.   B) good immediacy.

    C) good eye contact.   D) good nonverbal communication.

Answer: C
Page Ref: 281
Topic: Characteristics of effective delivery
Skill: Description Question

13) Which of the following statements is the best guideline for using gestures in a speech?

    A) Use as many gestures as possible in your presentation.

    B) Keep your hands clasped in front of you or in back of you.

    C) Every emotion can be expressed by a particular gesture.

    D) Make your gestures appropriate to the situation and audience.

Answer: D
Page Ref: 282
Topic: Characteristics of effective delivery
Skill: Description Question

14) By using appropriate levels of eye contact, moving purposefully, and smiling while talking, what behaviors is the speaker engaging in?

    A) delivery behaviors   B) immediacy behaviors

    C) concurrence behaviors   D) nonverbal behaviors

Answer: B
Page Ref: 284-285
Topic: Movement
Skill: Description Question

15) Of the three types of microphones, which type requires the most skill to use effectively?

    A) the stationary microphone   B) the lavaliere microphone

    C) the boom microphone   D) the cordless microphone

Answer: A
Page Ref: 290-291
Topic: Vocal delivery, using a microphone
Skill: Description Question

16) How does your text advise you to adapt your speech delivery style for television?

    A) Keep your gestures and your facial expressions toned down.

    B) Deliver your speech more formally than for a live audience.

    C) Wear clothing that will make you stand out from the crowd.

    D) Try to craft your message so that it will reach everyone.

Answer: A
Page Ref: 297-298
Topic: Adapting your speech delivery for television
Skill: Description Question

17) In a crowded arena, you notice that when others laugh, clap, or cheer on the speaker, you are more likely to follow along with their actions. This is an example of

    A) nonverbal expectancy theory.   B) emotional contagion theory.

    C) delivery theory.   D) collective assemblage theory.

Answer: B
Page Ref: 276
Topic: Power of speech delivery
Skill: Example Question

18) When Kelsey says, "How many of you have ever donated money to causes that support the homeless?" as she extends the palms of her hands toward the audience. Kelsey's nonverbal communication serves what function?

    A) emphasizing   B) repeating   C) regulating   D) substituting

Answer: C
Page Ref: 283
Topic: Characteristics of effective delivery, gestures
Skill: Example Question

19) The minister pounds his fist on the podium when he says the words "sin" and "evil." What function does this form of nonverbal communication serve?

    A) emphasizing   B) contradicting   C) regulating   D) complementing

Answer: A
Page Ref: 283
Topic: Characteristics of effective delivery, gestures
Skill: Example Question

20) Several studies have determined that the most effective teachers in North America

    A) pace back and forth to keep the class's attention.

    B) move from behind the podium only when making a point.

    C) use dramatic gestures to emphasize their points.

    D) are the ones who stand closer to their students.

Answer: D
Page Ref: 284–285
Topic: Movement
Skill: Example Question

21) Words such as "dint," "mornin," "gunna," and "wanna" are all examples of poor

    A) articulation.   B) dialect.   C) pronunciation.   D) regionalisms.

Answer: A
Page Ref: 287
Topic: Vocal delivery
Skill: Example Question

22) Knowing that he was speaking to a culturally diverse audience, Buck arrived early to his speaking engagement to hear the presentations of some international persons whom he knew would be in his audience later. What kind of observations are important for Buck to make in order to adapt his speech to that audience?

    A) Buck should observe the length of the previous speeches.

    B) Buck should observe the room and the arrangement.

    C) Buck should observe the speakers' eye contact and gestures.

    D) Buck should observe the dress style of previous speakers.

Answer: C
Page Ref: 293
Topic: Audience diversity and delivery
Skill: Example Question

23) Marian is speaking to a group from China, which she knows is a high-context culture. How should she adapt her delivery style to this culture?

    A) Marian should deliver her speech slowly with little movement.

    B) Marian should wear white because it stands out well.

    C) Marian should concentrate on her nonverbal delivery.

    D) Marian should use the same vocal inflection as they do.

Answer: C
Page Ref: 293
Topic: Adapting speech delivery for diverse audiences
Skill: Example Question

24) Reverend Charles is preparing his Sunday sermon. He wants to use a method of delivery that has the most potential for eye contact with the congregation, because he wants to really "drive home" his points on serving the homeless and less fortunate in the community. What method of delivery would be best?

   A) memorized speaking   B) manuscript speaking
   C) extemporaneous speaking   D) impromptu speaking

Answer: A
Page Ref: 277
Topic: Methods of delivery
Skill: Application Question

25) Given the task of preparing a speech, Susan decides to speak from an outline that can help her sound conversational and spontaneous. She wants to be able to adapt her remarks to the feedback she receives from the audience. She also wants to make more eye contact with the audience. What method of delivery will be best, given Susan's speech goals?

   A) memory speaking   B) extemporaneous speaking
   C) manuscript speaking   D) impromptu speaking

Answer: B
Page Ref: 279
Topic: Methods of delivery
Skill: Application Question

26) The audience could tell that Chad really didn't like his speech topic. At several points in the speech, he blushed, rolled his eyes, dipped his head, and shrugged his shoulders. What function were these nonverbal cues serving in this example?

   A) The nonverbal cues were complementing the verbal communication.

   B) The nonverbal cues were emphasizing the verbal communication.

   C) The nonverbal cues were substituting for verbal communication.

   D) The nonverbal cues were contradicting the verbal communication.

Answer: D
Page Ref: 283
Topic: Characteristics of effective delivery, gestures
Skill: Application Question

27) Savannah has a strong southern accent, which is appropriate because Savannah is from Georgia. But, according to your textbook authors, should Savannah try to tone down her dialect when she makes public presentations?

  A) No; if Savannah is proud of her southern heritage, she should sound like a southerner and not attempt to alter her vocal style.

  B) Yes; speakers should minimize any traces of regionalism in their vocal delivery so as to be understood by a wide variety of audiences.

  C) No; Savannah probably needs to slow down some to give non-southern audiences more potential for understanding, but she shouldn't get rid of her dialect.

  D) Yes, but only if Savannah's dialect is so pronounced that audiences can't understand her, then she should attempt to tone down her dialect.

Answer: D
Page Ref: 287-288
Topic: Vocal delivery
Skill: Application Question

28) Matthew presented a persuasive speech on achieving one's goals. He discussed ways that persons should challenge themselves in terms of striving for prominent positions in their communities, working hard to gain respectability in their jobs, and by being responsible citizens. Matthew used good movement, eye contact, vocal variation, and was dressed in khaki slacks and a polo-type shirt. According to your text, did Matthew make any delivery mistakes?

  A) No; he displayed the most important nonverbal elements in his speech delivery.

  B) Yes; he probably should have kept his vocal variation at a minimum, to appear professional and to heighten his credibility.

  C) Yes; he probably should have worn a tie and a more professional shirt, so that his speech topic and his appearance matched.

  D) No; the description of his delivery indicates that his speech topic and his nonverbal delivery were a good match.

Answer: C
Page Ref: 291
Topic: Characteristics of effective delivery
Skill: Application Question

29) In his speech about American loyalty and patriotism, Mike thought he had really reached everyone in his audience. However, after receiving classmates' written critiques of his speech, it seems as though his delivery and content offended a couple of international students in his class. Which of the following statements best explains this situation?

   A) Mike should have used a manuscript delivery rather than an extemporaneous one, so that he didn't run the risk of offending anyone in the audience.

   B) Mike didn't do anything wrong, because you just can't anticipate and cater to every single member of your audience.

   C) Mike's presentation likely contained an ethnocentric approach, one which has the potential to offend members of other cultures.

   D) Mike didn't do anything wrong, because members of minority cultures should adapt to the values and behaviors of the dominant culture when they travel abroad.

Answer: C
Page Ref: 293
Topic: Audience diversity and delivery
Skill: Application Question

30) Eric was an excellent cook and so decided to present a speech on "The American Art of Barbecue" to his Japanese audience. He was quite flamboyant with a chef's outfit, broad gestures, booming voice, and having an actual grill for the presentation. His audience did not seem to appreciate his speech. What could be the problem?

   A) Eric didn't realize that the Japanese only approve of chefs of Asian cuisine, like the Iron Chef.

   B) Eric didn't realize that the Japanese don't like barbecue because most of their foods are steamed, not grilled.

   C) Eric didn't realize that the Japanese are a high-context culture and consider his speech overdone.

   D) Eric didn't realize that his ideas were ethnocentric and offended he his Japanese audience.

Answer: C
Page Ref: 293
Topic: Audience diversity and delivery
Skill: Application Question

31) Shauna thought that she had a great speech. The speech was thoroughly researched and organized, with a good preparation and speaking outline ready to go. She read her outline to herself over and over before presenting it in class. When presenting her speech, she lost her place, stumbled over words, and dropped her visual aids. What important preparation step did Shauna skip?

    A) Shauna forgot to write delivery notes on her speaking outline.

    B) Shauna forget to memorize her speech and choreograph specific gestures.

    C) Shauna forgot to give herself positive reinforcement before her speech.

    D) Shauna forgot to rehearse her speech while standing up, presenting her ideas out loud, and practicing with her visual aids.

Answer: D
Page Ref: 294–295
Topic: Rehearsing your speech: some final tips
Skill: Application Question

32) Yvonne was really nervous about her upcoming speech. On the day of the speech, she arrived early, used mental and physical relaxation techniques, and felt like she knew the speech. But all she could think about was how the audience wouldn't laugh at her funny moments in the speech and how the applause would be weak and disappointing. What tip for reducing delivery jitters that your textbook advises did Yvonne ignore?

    A) A speaker should never arrive early for a speaking engagement; the tension of waiting around to deliver the speech will only add to the speaker's nervousness.

    B) Yvonne forgot to visualize her success; instead she visualized her failure.

    C) Yvonne obviously did not know her speech as well as she could have or else she would have been in control of her nerves.

    D) Yvonne didn't ignore any tips regarding delivery jitters; this kind of speaker nervousness is natural and to be expected.

Answer: B
Page Ref: 297
Topic: Rehearsing your speech, delivering your speech
Skill: Application Question

33) Most of the emotional content of a speech is communicated nonverbally.

Answer: TRUE
Page Ref: 274
Topic: The power of speech delivery

34) Both content and delivery contribute to the effectiveness of a speaker.

Answer: TRUE
Page Ref: 275
Topic: The power of speech delivery

35) Emotional contagion theory suggests that people tend to focus on their own emotions during a presentation.

Answer: FALSE
Page Ref: 276
Topic: The power of speech delivery

36) With an extemporaneous delivery a speaker uses a written or memorized speech outline having memorized the exact wording of the speech.

Answer: FALSE
Page Ref: 279
Topic: Extemporaneous speaking

37) Extemporaneous speaking and impromptu speaking are the same thing.

Answer: FALSE
Page Ref: 277–279
Topic: Methods of delivery

38) Most audiences in the United States prefer that you don't establish eye contact with them before speaking because the eye contact can intimidate the audience and make them anxious.

Answer: FALSE
Page Ref: 281
Topic: Characteristics of effective delivery

39) The process of producing clear and distinct sounds is pronunciation.

Answer: FALSE
Page Ref: 287
Topic: Vocal delivery

40) Silence can be an effective tool in emphasizing a particular word or sentence.

Answer: TRUE
Page Ref: 290
Topic: Vocal delivery, speaking with variety

41) Vocalized pauses such as "you know" are used by so many speakers that they are not noticeable.

Answer: FALSE
Page Ref: 290
Topic: Vocal delivery, speaking with variety

42) Ethnocentrism means that you value other cultures more than you value your own.

Answer: FALSE
Page Ref: 293
Topic: Audience diversity and delivery

43) Briefly explain nonverbal expectancy theory and emotional contagion theory and their impact on public speaking.

Page Ref: 275
Topic: The power of speech delivery

44) What are the main differences between manuscript speaking and extemporaneous speaking?

Page Ref: 276-277, 279
Topic: Methods of delivery

45) Describe how gestures can be used effectively in a speech.

Page Ref: 282-284
Topic: Characteristics of effective delivery, gestures

46) Identify and explain three guidelines a speaker should follow when making a televised presentation.

Page Ref: 297-298
Topic: Adapting your speech delivery for television

47) There are four primary methods of speech delivery. In a well-developed essay, identify the four methods. Then provide two advantages and two disadvantages connected to using each method.

Page Ref: 276-279
Topic: Methods of delivery

48) Of the six functions of gestures discussed in your text, define five and give examples of how each could be used effectively in a speech.

Page Ref: 282-284
Topic: Characteristics of effective delivery, gestures

49) The diversity of your audience has a significant impact on your speech. In a well-developed essay, discuss what your textbook identifies as four strategies for adapting your verbal and nonverbal delivery to a multicultural audience.

Page Ref: 293-294
Topic: Audience diversity and delivery

50) Realizing that all public speakers are nervous to some extent or another, the authors of your textbook have provided four ways to help you reduce that last-minute nervousness a speaker will inevitably feel. In a detailed essay, discuss these four suggestions; then describe how each can have a positive effect on a speaker's confidence and control of nerves.

Page Ref: 295-297
Topic: Delivering your speech

Chapter 14 Using Presentation Aids

1) Of the five senses, presentational aids are effective because we depend on _____ more than any other sense.

   A) hearing   B) sight   C) touch   D) humor

   Answer: B
   Page Ref: 306
   Topic: The value of presentation aids
   Skill: Definition Question

2) The most unpredictable presentation aid a speaker could use is

   A) *PowerPoint.*   B) transparencies.

   C) a person or animal.   D) videos.

   Answer: C
   Page Ref: 309
   Topic: Types of presentation aids
   Skill: Definition Question

3) This type of presentational aid can be effective especially if the speaker personalizes it by highlighting relevant information; but remember, the specific detail won't be legible or visible to the audience unless it is enlarged.

   A) maps   B) slides   C) charts   D) graphs

   Answer: A
   Page Ref: 311
   Topic: Types of presentation aids
   Skill: Definition Question

4) A presentation aid which is a representation of statistical data is

   A) a graph.   B) a drawing.   C) a model.   D) a slide.

   Answer: A
   Page Ref: 311
   Topic: Types of presentation aids
   Skill: Definition Question

5) A graph that uses images to symbolize the data that appears on the graph is known as a

   A) chart.   B) bar graph.   C) line graph.   D) picture graph.

   Answer: D
   Page Ref: 312
   Topic: Types of presentation aids
   Skill: Definition Question

6) A presentation aid that displays information in the form of words, numbers, or images is

    A) a graph.   B) a visual.   C) a chart.   D) a transparency.

Answer: C
Page Ref: 313
Topic: Types of presentation aids
Skill: Definition Question

7) The presentational aid that is prepared ahead of time, can be marked on while speaking, and allows the speaker to maintain eye contact while speaking is

    A) a flipchart.   B) a transparency.   C) a model.   D) a chart.

Answer: B
Page Ref: 315
Topic: Types of presentation aids
Skill: Definition Question

8) When considering the use of fonts in presentation aids, you should know that a sans serif font

    A) is better for reading longer passages.

    B) has no added lines at the top and bottom.

    C) is a decoration type font.

    D) looks like handwriting.

Answer: B
Page Ref: 318–319
Topic: Types of presentation aids, choose a typeface with care
Skill: Definition Question

9) From the following options, the best reason to use presentation aids is

    A) they cover up a speaker's visible nervousness.

    B) they help your audience understand and remember.

    C) they can substitute for a general lack of information.

    D) they can help a speaker stay within the time limit.

Answer: B
Page Ref: 306
Topic: The value of presentation aids
Skill: Description Question

10) The type of speech that will benefit from the use of presentation aids is

    A) an informative speech.   B) any type of speech.

    C) a persuasive speech.   D) a motivational speech.

Answer: B
Page Ref: 306
Topic: Using presentation aids
Skill: Description Question

11) The best reason that presentation aids enhance an audience's memory of the speech is that

    A) presentation aids can be quite colorful and, therefore, memorable.

    B) audience members will better understand and remember the speech because of visual reinforcement.

    C) audiences rarely listen when someone is just talking.

    D) presentation aids are simple to produce and show the audience.

Answer: B
Page Ref: 307
Topic: The value of presentation aids
Skill: Description Question

12) What does your text advise regarding using people as presentation aids in a speech?

    A) Never use other people as presentation aids in a speech because of the potential for something to go wrong.

    B) Rehearse with the person and avoid using the spur-of-the-moment volunteer in the speech.

    C) Make sure they don't draw away from your speech; have them stand or sit still until they are needed in the speech.

    D) Avoid using others as presentational aids; rely on yourself as the presentational aid.

Answer: B
Page Ref: 309
Topic: Types of presentation aids
Skill: Description Question

13) How can a photograph best be used as a presentation aid?

    A) Pass it around to the entire audience.

    B) Make copies of it and hand the copies out.

    C) Put it on a transparency or *PowerPoint*.

    D) Put it in a large, attention-getting frame.

Answer: C
Page Ref: 310
Topic: Types of presentation aids
Skill: Description Question

14) Why would a picture graph be used in a speech?

    A) To summarize statistical information which will be clear and immediately visible to the audience.

    B) To show the audience how statistical data are distributed in a given category or area.

    C) To represent statistical data and trends over a given period of time.

    D) To present data in a less formal format which is easier for the audience to read.

Answer: D
Page Ref: 312
Topic: Types of presentation aids
Skill: Description Question

15) What does the textbook suggest if the speech topic calls for an illegal or dangerous presentation aid?

    A) Secure permission from the instructor well before the speech day.

    B) Secure written permission from police or security officers.

    C) Take all necessary precautions; warn your audience before the speech.

    D) Substitute with an appropriate model, picture, or other presentational device.

Answer: D
Page Ref: 324
Topic: Guidelines for developing presentation aids
Skill: Description Question

16) When using a presentational aid, there is always the possibility of "something going wrong" while you are speaking. If something does go wrong, what should you do as a speaker?

    A) Use presentational aids sparingly; they become a distraction otherwise.

    B) The speech will be interrupted and the audience will lose focus; end the speech shortly after that distraction.

    C) Offer a lengthy apology for the distraction and then continue on with the speech.

    D) Have back up supplies and a back up plan in case your best–laid plans go awry.

Answer: D
Page Ref: 327
Topic: Guidelines for using presentation aids
Skill: Description Question

17) Listing your main ideas on a transparency or computer program such as *PowerPoint* best illustrates which use of presentation aids, according to your text?

    A) helping to persuade listeners to your point of view

    B) helping listeners keep your ideas organized

    C) helping to illustrate technical, complicated procedures

    D) helping to smooth your own delivery

Answer: B
Page Ref: 307
Topic: The value of presentation aids
Skill: Example Question

18) Which of the following is an example of a two–dimensional presentation aid?

    A) a model of the human heart   B) a puppy dog

    C) a graph of population growth   D) a set of golf clubs

Answer: C
Page Ref: 310
Topic: Types of presentation aids
Skill: Example Question

19) Although computer-generated PowerPoint presentations are gaining popularity as visual aids, overhead projectors remain popular for speakers. According to the text, why does this hold true?

    A) With budget constraints, this is a cost-effective solution for many companies.

    B) Overhead projectors are widely available; most organizations have and maintain these projectors.

    C) A great deal of information can be printed on the transparency, thus allowing the speaker to stay within their time limit.

    D) Speakers are able to maintain eye contact with the audience while also being able to see the visual.

Answer: D
Page Ref: 315
Topic: Types of presentation aids
Skill: Example Question

20) When developing an effective PowerPoint visual, what must speakers consider?

    A) Audience members like a lot of movement and action so a number of slides will maintain audience attention.

    B) Different font sizes and font types add visual interest.

    C) Color may be added to the slides to communicate warmth or coolness.

    D) Being that this is computer generated, the presentation can be put together just before speaking.

Answer: C
Page Ref: 316–317
Topic: Types of presentation aids
Skill: Example Question

21) Shiloh was presenting a speech about the different types of classical music. He had a transparency of each type covered and played a selection of that music as he revealed and explained each type. Had Shiloh planned well for his use of presentation aids?

    A) Yes; he used a combination of different types of aids effectively.

    B) Yes; audiences always enjoy hearing music in a speech.

    C) No; he had too many presentation aids to handle.

    D) No; college students don't usually appreciate classical music.

Answer: A
Page Ref: 322
Topic: Guidelines for using presentation aids
Skill: Example Question

22) On her way to public speaking class, Delaney decided to add one last presentation aid to her speech. Was this a good idea, according to your textbook?

  A) Yes; the more creative the presentation aids, the better the speech will be.

  B) Yes; if Delaney was certain that the presentation aid would make a difference.

  C) No; because Delaney didn't have a chance to rehearse with the new aid.

  D) No; because the extra presentation aid would make Delaney's speech run over time.

Answer: C
Page Ref: 324
Topic: Guidelines for using presentation aids
Skill: Example Question

23) Kayt had carefully planned presentation aids for her speech on "Quilting." She thoroughly demonstrated how to sew together the squares by hand, which required her to concentrate on the quilt. What guideline for using presentation aids did Kayt violate?

  A) Kayt did not select the right presentation aid for her audience.

  B) Kayt did not rehearse with her visual aid before the presentation.

  C) Kayt focused on the presentation aid instead of the audience.

  D) Kayt should have passed a finished quilt square around to the class instead.

Answer: C
Page Ref: 324
Topic: Guidelines for using presentation aids
Skill: Example Question

24) Elaine taped pictures of her Aruba vacation all around the room as presentation aids for her speech. She never referred to them, but simply created an atmosphere for his presentation. Was this appropriate?

  A) Yes; the pictures created the kind of mood she wanted.

  B) Yes, because these pictures were relaxing images and helped the audience listen.

  C) No; there were too many of them to create any kind of effect.

  D) No, because she should have explained the presentation aids, not just show them.

Answer: D
Page Ref: 325
Topic: Guidelines for using presentation aids
Skill: Example Question

25) Joe is a member of Future Farmers of America (FFA), so for his demonstration speech he wanted to show his audience the proper way to groom and care for his prize-winning Holstein cattle. Instead of bringing a Holstein to class, what does the textbook suggest Joe should do in this demonstration speech?

    A) Joe should use pictures since the actual object is too large and cumbersome to be easily used as a presentation aid for this speech.

    B) Joe should forego the use of presentation aids in such a situation since a large presentation aid (such as a cow) would be too distracting.

    C) Joe should use a three-dimensional model of a Holstein along with the items he uses to groom the cattle when the actual object is too large to be easily used as a presentation aid for a speech.

    D) Joe should go ahead and use the Holstein, even if it is large and not easy to maneuver, because an object is always preferable to a drawing or model.

Answer: C
Page Ref: 309, 325
Topic: Types of aids, guidelines for using presentation aids
Skill: Application Question

26) In Louise's speech about various golf grips and strokes, Louise used several golf clubs and demonstrated the moves herself. According to your textbook's guidelines on the use of presentation aids, was this a good technique?

    A) Yes; a speaker can serve as a presentation aid to demonstrate how something works or is done.

    B) Yes, but only if other objects or charts are used in conjunction with the speaker's movements.

    C) No; Louise should have used someone else to demonstrate, so that he could keep speaking.

    D) No; demonstrations like this are distracting and too informal for a public speech.

Answer: A
Page Ref: 308-309
Topic: Types of presentation aids
Skill: Application Question

27) Regina's demonstration speech topic was "Three Ways to Improved Photography." In this speech, Regina showed a 35 mm camera, used a chart with an enlarged diagram of the main components of the camera, and then showed 4 x 6 photographs—some good and some with errors—to the audience. Which of the following statements best summarizes Regina's use of presentation aids in this speech?

    A) Regina selected and handled all of her presentation aids expertly in this speech.

    B) Regina should not have brought the camera; the diagram was sufficient.

    C) Regina showed good audience and environmental analysis in her use of presentation aids.

    D) Regina should have enlarged the photographs so the audience could clearly see them.

Answer: D
Page Ref: 310
Topic: Types of presentation aids
Skill: Application Question

28) Dwayne is giving an informative speech about methods of increasing memory capacity. He has four steps, each starting with a catchy word, such as Stop, Repeat, etc. What is the best way for Dwayne to help his audience retain his information?

    A) He should use a detailed bar graph demonstrating how memory capacity can be expanded.

    B) He should use vivid pictures and drawings to create mental images for his audience.

    C) He should avoid presentation aids because they will distract the audience from his message.

    D) He should enumerate the four steps on a transparency or *PowerPoint* to reinforce his message.

Answer: D
Page Ref: 315-317
Topic: Types of presentation aids
Skill: Application Question

29) Indar wanted to do really well on his speech, so he decided to use his new *PowerPoint* software to help him generate effective computer graphics. He hadn't had time to really learn the process yet, but he felt like he could learn enough to get by in the presentation. When it came time for the speech, Indar couldn't make the computer program work like he wanted. What was Indar's biggest mistake?

    A) Indar should have used more conventional methods of designing presentation aids; computer wizardry is highly over-rated.

    B) Indar should have had someone else run the computer, because requiring that a speaker run a computer program while delivering a speech is too much to ask.

    C) Indar should have learned the computer program well in advance of the speech, or else have decided to use a presentation aid method he was more comfortable with for the presentation.

    D) Indar really made no mistake in this situation; sometimes the best-laid plans can go awry, especially when computers are involved.

Answer: C
Page Ref: 320
Topic: Types of presentation aids
Skill: Application Question

30) Kevin is preparing for a speech to a very large audience—some 500 people at a professional conference. He has plenty of technology available in the room he'll be speaking in, but he thinks he'll just use an overhead projector and several overhead transparencies containing outlines of his main points. Which of the following statements best pertains to this situation?

    A) Kevin is right about using overheads, because overhead transparencies will keep it simple and clear for his audience.

    B) Kevin should use a series of large, colorful posters and charts, spread around the auditorium instead of overheads, so that he doesn't have to darken the room.

    C) Kevin should forget about the presentation aids, because a dynamic delivery can substitute for any positive effects visual aids could produce.

    D) Kevin should use computer-generated graphics displayed on a large screen, for maximum attention and retention from his audience.

Answer: D
Page Ref: 322
Topic: Guidelines for using presentation aids
Skill: Application Question

31) In a speech about organ donation, Nathan gave the audience a handout about the need for organs and the process for becoming an organ donor before his speech. Is this an effective use of presentation aids, according to the text's guidelines?

    A) Yes; Nathan drew the audience into the speech by having them focus on the handout.

    B) No; Nathan should have waited until the conclusion to hand this out as audience members will read what you give them.

    C) No; Nathan confused the audience by having them look at a handout that didn't relate to what he was speaking about.

    D) Yes; Nathan used the handout in a timely and effective way, selecting the right presentation aid for the topic.

Answer: B
Page Ref: 325–326
Topic: Guidelines for using presentation aids
Skill: Application Question

32) Rashan thought that he would be dramatic and impress his public speaking class with his speech on dog training. He decided to bring in his german shepherd to illustrate the points and techniques of obedience. But during the speech, he noticed that the audience's attention was on his dog, rather than on him as the speaker. What guideline did Rashan ignore, with regard to using presentation aids?

    A) Do not use dangerous or illegal presentation aids.

    B) Never use animals as presentation aids in a speech.

    C) Use animals with caution as presentation aids.

    D) Only use ugly animals so the audience will ignore them.

Answer: C
Page Ref: 325
Topic: Guidelines for using presentation aids
Skill: Application Question

33) If your purpose is to inform your audience about a process, then the best way to demonstrate this is with a set of visuals or demonstrations.

Answer: TRUE
Page Ref: 307
Topic: The value of presentation aids

34) With the predominance of media images on TV, in the movies, on the internet, and now even on our phones, images are central to how we receive information.

Answer: TRUE
Page Ref: 306–307
Topic: The value of presentation aids

35) When using maps in a speech, it is a good idea to make copies for everyone in the audience.

Answer: FALSE
Page Ref: 311
Topic: Types of presentation aids

36) Charts should contain a great deal of information so the audience members can easily follow along with the speaker.

Answer: FALSE
Page Ref: 313-314
Topic: Types of presentation aids

37) The chalkboard is an excellent visual aid since it has great versatility.

Answer: FALSE
Page Ref: 314-315
Topic: Types of presentation aids

38) If a speaker has presented the major points in the speech, and uses internal summaries, listing these on an transparency or *PowerPoint* will bore the audience.

Answer: FALSE
Page Ref: 315-317
Topic: Types of presentation aids

39) Presentation aids *support* your message; they are not your message.

Answer: TRUE
Page Ref: 317
Topic: Types of presentation aids

40) Repeating a visual element, such as a bullet or visual symbol at the beginning of each word on a list, will help to unify your presentation.

Answer: TRUE
Page Ref: 317-318
Topic: Repeat visual elements to unify presentations

41) With the advent of DVD recorders, DVDs can be made by the speaker and used in any DVD player as a presentation aid.

Answer: FALSE
Page Ref: 321
Topic: Digital video disks

42) Complex and detailed presentation aids are usually the best way to communicate in a presentation.

Answer: FALSE
Page Ref: 322-323
Topic: Guidelines for developing presentation aids

43) Using the hypothetical speech topic, "How to Pack for a Trip," offer examples of the three types of three-dimensional presentation aids your textbook discusses that would be effective in this speech.

Page Ref: 308-309
Topic: Types of presentation aids

44) Explain how a bar graph, a pie graph, a line graph, and a picture graph serve different purposes as presentation aids.

Page Ref: 311-312
Topic: Types of presentation aids

45) List and briefly explain the tips the textbook offers for developing an effective PowerPoint visual.

Page Ref: 316-317
Topic: Types of presentation aids

46) List and briefly discuss the four ways to select the right presentation aids for your speech.

Page Ref: 323
Topic: Select the right presentation aids

47) What are the guidelines, according to your text, for using handouts effectively?

Page Ref: 325-326
Topic: Use handouts effectively

48) Your textbook describes five ways that presentation aids are invaluable to a speaker. In a well-developed essay, identify and explain these five ways.

Page Ref: 306-307
Topic: The value of presentation aids

49) Ten general types of two-dimensional presentation aids are discussed in your text. Using the hypothetical speech topic, "Voter Trends in My Home State," explain how you would use three of the ten types of presentation aids to enhance this speech. Then explain why three *other* types of two-dimensional aids would not be as effective.

Page Ref: 310-320
Topic: Two-dimensional presentation aids

50) In a speech about developing effective study habits, your classmate George has chosen three presentation aids to enhance his audience's retention of his information: (1) a chart summarizing basic steps of creating an appropriate study environment; (2) a graph showing how improved study skills translates into higher grades; and (3) a book and a highlighter. Of the nine guidelines for the use of presentation aids provided in your text, select five that will be the most relevant to George's speech. In a well-developed essay, explain how these five guidelines should be applied and how they will make the speech more successful.

Page Ref: 324-327
Topic: Guidelines for using presentation aids

Chapter 15   Speaking to Inform

1) In a speech with the general purpose "to inform," a speaker's goal is
   A) to act as an advocate for an issue.   B) to be a storyteller, sharing experiences.
   C) to teach others new information.   D) to motivate the audience to act.

   Answer: C
   Page Ref: 334
   Topic: Speaking to inform
   Skill: Definition Question

2) When trying to help the audience make sense of the information being presented, the goal of
   the speaker should be to
   A) make sure they are heard, enhance understanding, and connect nonverbally with the
      audience.
   B) allow the audience time to listen, increase understanding, and have visuals for them to
      remember.
   C) enhance understanding, gain interest, and ensure that the audience will remember what
      was said.
   D) enhance listening, ensure that the audience will learn, and have the audience apply the
      knowledge.

   Answer: C
   Page Ref: 335
   Topic: Speaking to enhance understanding
   Skill: Definition Question

3) An informative speech that discusses anything you can see or touch is a speech about
   A) procedures.   B) ideas.   C) people.   D) objects.

   Answer: D
   Page Ref: 336
   Topic: Types of informative speeches
   Skill: Definition Question

4) An informative speech that discusses how something works, or describes a process with a
   particular outcome, is a speech about
   A) procedures.   B) objects.   C) people.   D) ideas.

   Answer: A
   Page Ref: 337
   Topic: Types of informative speeches
   Skill: Definition Question

5) In this type of informative speech you could talk about someone famous or someone you know. This is known as a

    A) biological speech.   B) genealogy speech.

    C) historical speech.   D) biographical speech

Answer: D
Page Ref: 338
Topic: Types of informative speeches
Skill: Definition Question

6) To express your ideas so that the intended message is accurately understood by the audience is known as

    A) simplification.   B) audience analysis.

    C) clarity.   D) precision.

Answer: C
Page Ref: 341
Topic: Strategies to enhance audience understanding
Skill: Definition Question

7) The art and science of teaching children to learn is

    A) pedagogy.   B) andragogy.   C) analogy.   D) ideology.

Answer: A
Page Ref: 342
Topic: Use principles and techniques of adult learning
Skill: Definition Question

8) The art and science of teaching adults to learn is

    A) pedagogy.   B) andragogy.   C) analogy.   D) ideology.

Answer: B
Page Ref: 342
Topic: Andragogy
Skill: Definition Question

9) When a speaker shows the audience that the information presented will affect them directly, he or she is fulfilling which goal of information speaking?

    A) to enhance understanding   B) to maintain interest

    C) to be remembered   D) to be heard

Answer: B
Page Ref: 335
Topic: Goals of informative speaking
Skill: Description Question

10) When you carefully select your words, examples, and illustrations, you are speaking to

   A) to maintain interest   B) to be remembered

   C) to enhance understanding   D) to be entertaining

Answer: A
Page Ref: 335
Topic: Goals of informative speaking
Skill: Description Question

11) By being organized, using appropriate redundancy, internal summaries, and relating the information to the audience, the goal of your informative speech is to

   A) enhance understanding.   B) maintain interest.

   C) be remembered.   D) motivate your audience to action

Answer: C
Page Ref: 335–336
Topic: Goals of informative speaking
Skill: Description Question

12) What kind of speech focuses on a process or how something works?

   A) a speech about an event   B) a speech about a procedure

   C) a speech about an object   D) a speech about a person

Answer: B
Page Ref: 337–338
Topic: Types of informative speeches
Skill: Description Question

13) An informative speech about an event typically follows this pattern of organization.

   A) chronological   B) topical

   C) problem–solution   D) spatial

Answer: A
Page Ref: 339
Topic: Types of informative speeches
Skill: Description Question

14) This term means *comparisons* and is usually a good for giving listeners the big picture before going into great detail:

   A) analogies   B) similarities   C) clarifying   D) andragogy

Answer: A
Page Ref: 342
Topic: Strategies to enhance audience understanding
Skill: Description Question

15) One way in which adults learn differently from children is that adults
    A) like to be actively involved in the learning process.
    B) like to learn new information that is beyond their experience.
    C) like to learn about material that focuses on abstract ideas and concepts.
    D) like to learn as little as possible.

Answer: A
Page Ref: 342
Topic: Strategies to enhance audience understanding
Skill: Description Question

16) That adult learners like to know how new information presented is relevant to their needs and lives is one of the principles of
    A) pedagogy.   B) andragogy.   C) analogy.   D) ideology.

Answer: B
Page Ref: 342
Topic: Strategies to enhance audience understanding
Skill: Description Question

17) Phyllis presented an informative speech on how to fix a flat tire. What type of informative speech was this?
    A) a speech about an idea   B) a speech about a procedure
    C) a speech about an object   D) a speech about an event

Answer: B
Page Ref: 337–338
Topic: Types of informative speeches
Skill: Example Question

18) Roberto gave an informative speech about the life and artistic accomplishments of Andy Warhol. What type of informative speech did Roberto deliver?
    A) a speech about an idea   B) a speech about an event
    C) a speech about people   D) a speech about a procedure

Answer: C
Page Ref: 338
Topic: Types of informative speeches
Skill: Example Question

19) Seth decided to present his informative speech on the origins and development of the Mardi Gras parades. What type of informative speech did Seth present?
    A) a speech about an idea   B) a speech about an event
    C) a speech about people   D) a speech about a procedure

Answer: B
Page Ref: 339
Topic: Types of informative speeches
Skill: Example Question

20) When previewing your speech on Islam, you say, "The best way to understand Islam is to look at some of the beliefs and practices of this religion." You will be giving a speech about

    A) a procedure.   B) people.   C) an event.   D) an idea

Answer: D
Page Ref: 339-340
Topic: Types of informative speeches
Skill: Example Question

21) In her speech about small pox, Jessica previewed her ideas in the introduction, summarized key points throughout the speech, and provided a visual outline on an overhead. What public speaking principle did Jessica apply?

    A) She used the principle of pedagogy.

    B) She used the principle of speaking with clarity.

    C) She used the principle of andragogy.

    D) She used the principle of audience analysis.

Answer: B
Page Ref: 341
Topic: Strategies to enhance audience understanding
Skill: Example Question

22) In an informative speech to a group of high school juniors, Tori talked about how college can change your life, about the change in her confidence level from her first year to her senior year. Although college seemed a long way off for her audience, they listened intently. Tori made her speech interesting by

    A) telling a story that had conflict and suspense.

    B) presenting information that related to their lives.

    C) asking them a rhetorical question.

    D) presenting information that was startling.

Answer: B
Page Ref: 346
Topic: Strategies to maintain audience interest
Skill: Example Question

23) An effective way to keep an audience's attention is to tell a story. According to your text, what are three elements that make a good story?

    A) conflict, action, suspense   B) characters, plot, action

    C) conflict, dialogue, action   D) action, suspense, dialogue

Answer: A
Page Ref: 345-346
Topic: Strategies to maintain audience interest
Skill: Example Question

24) David decided to present his informative speech on "How to Give the The Heimlich maneuver." He opened by recounting a story of how he had saved his younger brother's life when his brother was choking on gum he had accidentally swallowed. Which of the goals of informative speaking was David targeting with this statement?

    A) defining a term by using a specific example

    B) developing a strategy to help the audience remember

    C) motivating the audience to listen through telling a story

    D) clarifying concepts to enhance understanding

Answer: C
Page Ref: 345
Topic: Strategies to maintain audience interest
Skill: Example Question

25) Gus was asked to present information on the topic of art appreciation. This topic can be rather vague and subjective in nature; different pieces of art can be described in a multitude of ways. However, Gus found a way of clearly defining terms and concepts so the audience would

have a common point of reference. For Gus, the primary goal of his informative speech would be

    A) to enhance understanding

    B) to maintain interest

    C) to have the audience remember the information

    D) to have the audience become art critics

Answer: A
Page Ref: 335
Topic: Goals of informative speaking
Skill: Application Question

26) When Chloe told a story about her mother's illness, you could have heard a pin drop in the room. The audience was riveted because she described her own emotions in coping with the physical and emotional stress through the whole experience, using vivid language and examples to make the experience more real. What type of informative speech did Chloe give?

    A) a speech about procedures   B) a speech about people

    C) a speech about events   D) a speech about ideas

Answer: C
Page Ref: 339
Topic: Types of informative speeches
Skill: Application Question

27) Montriece stood before a room filled with high school Seniors and their parents. In his introduction he stated, "I come before you today, not as a financial consultant, but as a former college student myself. It has been some time since I've been in a college classroom as a student, but I can clearly remember the financial struggles of being a student. Today, I'm going to present to you five ways you can cut costs for a college education." Why would this be a good opening for this audience?

   A) Because he reinforced the key ideas verbally.

   B) Because he built in redundancy.

   C) Because he had a good pace to the information.

   D) Because he established a motive for the audience to listen further.

   Answer: D
   Page Ref: 344
   Topic: Strategies to maintain audience interest
   Skill: Application Question

28) Your informative speech is about couples and romantic compatibility. In order to help listeners understand what you mean by "compatibility," you describe a quiz in a popular magazine. Couples take the quiz; the resulting score shows how compatible they are. What textbook strategy for maintaining audience interest was used?

   A) establishing a motive for the audience to listen

   B) telling a story

   C) present information that relates to the audience

   D) redundancy

   Answer: C
   Page Ref: 346
   Topic: Strategies to maintain audience interest
   Skill: Application Question

29) Sheena presented her informative speech on the life of Marie Curie. She had decided to cover Curie's early life and marriage, her scientific achievements despite the prejudice against her as a woman, and finally, the importance of Curie's discoveries on our lives today. She concluded her introduction by previewing all the main points, then used an internal summary as a transition to each of the main ideas. In her conclusion, she summarized her main ideas, emphasizing the importance of Marie Curie's life. What strategy to enhance audience recall was Sheena using?

   A) Pace the information flow.   B) Reinforce the main ideas nonverbally.

   C) Tell a suspenseful story.   D) Build in redundancy.

   Answer: D
   Page Ref: 346–347
   Topic: Strategies to enhance audience recall
   Skill: Application Question

30) Jason is informing the audience about an impending tuition hike at the college. Jason says, "Please, listen to this. This is important and affects all of us in this room; it affects our attitudes about school, our pocketbooks, and our stress levels." This strategy to enhance audience recall is

    A) building redundancy into the speech.   B) reinforcing key ideas verbally.

    C) reinforcing key ideas nonverbally.   D) pacing the information flow.

Answer: B
Page Ref: 347
Topic: Strategies to enhance audience recall
Skill: Application Question

31) When Kiko reviewed the main points in her informative speech, she slowed down her rate of speech, decreased her volume, made sure to articulate each word clearly, and paused between each point. What technique of enhancing audience recall did Kiko effectively employ?

    A) building redundancy into the speech   B) reinforcing key ideas verbally

    C) reinforcing key ideas nonverbally   D) pacing the flow of information

Answer: C
Page Ref: 347
Topic: Strategies to enhance audience recall
Skill: Application Question

32) Kelly really prided himself on his knowledge of British royal history. He had three main points in his informative speech, his first being the ancient lineage of Queen Elizabeth. By the time he got through his first point, his audience looked bored from all these facts. What was Kelly's error in this situation?

    A) not building redundancy into the speech

    B) not reinforcing his key ideas verbally

    C) not reinforcing his key ideas nonverbally

    D) not pacing the flow of his information

Answer: D
Page Ref: 347
Topic: Strategies to enhance audience recall
Skill: Application Question

33) It is more important in persuasive speaking to be audience-centered than in informative speaking.

Answer: FALSE
Page Ref: 334
Topic: Goals of informative speaking

34) The primary goals of informative speaking are to present information that the audience can understand and remember, while maintaining their interest.

Answer: TRUE
Page Ref: 335
Topic: Goals of informative speaking

35) Speeches about objects are usually more abstract than other types of informative speeches.

Answer: FALSE
Page Ref: 336
Topic: Types of informative speeches

36) Speaking about processes or procedures are usually arranged in chronological order.

Answer: TRUE
Page Ref: 337–338
Topic: Types of informative speeches

37) Informative speeches about events typically follow a cause–effect type of organizational pattern.

Answer: FALSE
Page Ref: 339
Topic: Types of informative speeches

38) Most informative speeches about ideas are organized topically.

Answer: TRUE
Page Ref: 339–340
Topic: Types of informative speeches

39) To speak with clarity is to express ideas so that the listener understands the intended message accurately.

Answer: TRUE
Page Ref: 341
Topic: Strategies to enhance audience understanding

40) When putting an informative speech together the speaker doesn't have to worry about speaking with clarity as long as there is a visual outline on PowerPoint for the audience to follow.

Answer: FALSE
Page Ref: 341
Topic: Speak with clarity

41) According to the text, adults are problem–oriented learners.

Answer: TRUE
Page Ref: 342
Topic: Use principles and techniques of adult learning

42) If you are trying to tell your listeners about a complex process, you only need clear and concise definitions to explain what you mean.

Answer: FALSE
Page Ref: 342
Topic: Clarify complex processes

43) Name and give examples of the five types of informative speeches.

Page Ref: 336–340
Topic: Types of informative speeches

44) List and briefly explain the strategies used by a speaker in order to speak with clarity.

Page Ref: 341
Topic: Speak with clarity

45) Briefly discuss the principles and techniques that are necessary when addressing the adult learner.

Page Ref: 342
Topic: Principles and techniques of adult learning

46) If a speaker were to present information on a complex process, what might they do to clarify that information for the audience? Present a brief explanation.

Page Ref: 342–344
Topic: Clarify complex processes

47) Identify and briefly define the four ways your textbook provides for enhancing audience recall in an informative speech.

Page Ref: 346–347
Topic: Strategies to enhance audience recall

48) Your textbook explains three goals of informative speaking. In an extensive essay, identify these goals and explain how each can be effectively accomplished by being "audience-centered."

Page Ref: 335–336
Topic: Goals of informative speaking

49) Imagine that your informative speech topic is "Hurricanes in the Atlantic." In a creative, thorough essay, explain the strategies a speaker would use to enhance audience understanding.

Page Ref: 341–344
Topic: Strategies to enhance audience understanding

50) It is critical to the success of an informative speech that the audience remember the speaker's information. Your textbook suggests four ways that a speaker can work to enhance audience recall. In a well-developed essay, discuss each of these and how they can enhance the audience's recall.

Page Ref: 346–347
Topic: Strategies to enhance audience recall

Chapter 16 Understanding Principles
of Persuasive Speaking

1) The process of changing or reinforcing a listener's attitudes, beliefs, values, or behavior is

    A) persuasion.   B) logic.   C) argument.   D) motivation.

Answer: A
Page Ref: 354
Topic: Persuasion defined
Skill: Definition Question

2) Our likes and dislikes are represented by our

    A) reasoning.   B) attitudes.   C) beliefs.   D) values.

Answer: B
Page Ref: 355
Topic: Persuasion defined
Skill: Definition Question

3) Something that is reinforced by past experiences and evidence is

    A) reason.   B) attitude.   C) belief.   D) value.

Answer: C
Page Ref: 355
Topic: Persuasion defined
Skill: Definition Question

4) The underlying internal force that drives us to achieve our goals is

    A) guilt.   B) persistence.   C) anxiety.   D) motivation

Answer: D
Page Ref: 356
Topic: How persuasion works
Skill: Definition Question

5) The sense of disorganization that prompts a person to change when new information conflicts with previously organized thought patterns.

    A) cognitive confusion.   B) cognitive dissonance.

    C) logical dissonance.   D) reasonable disassociation.

Answer: B
Page Ref: 357–358
Topic: How to motivate listeners
Skill: Definition Question

6) The personal need to achieve our highest potential is
    A) self esteem.   B) emotional values.
    C) self actualization.   D) psychological need.

Answer: C
Page Ref: 361
Topic: Use listener needs
Skill: Definition Question

7) Knowing what your listeners value or need and appealing to those values or needs is known in persuasion as
    A) self actualization appeal.   B) self esteem appeal.
    C) negative motivation.   D) positive motivation.

Answer: D
Page Ref: 361
Topic: Use positive motivation
Skill: Definition Question

8) The theory that categorizes listener responses to a persuasive message according to latitude of acceptance, latitude of rejection, or latitude of non-commitment.
    A) Social Exchange Theory.   B) Social Judgment Theory.
    C) Social Justice Theory.   D) Social Interaction Theory.

Answer: B
Page Ref: 366
Topic: Determine your persuasive purpose
Skill: Definition Question

9) With an informative speech the speaker informs about potential options available to the audience; persuasive speakers
    A) ask the audience members to make an explicit choice.
    B) teach the audience about the topic.
    C) focus on the goals of understanding and remembering.
    D) need well chosen words, transitions, and good delivery.

Answer: A
Page Ref: 354
Topic: Persuasion defined
Skill: Description Question

10) Persuasion is the process of

    A) motivating the audience to make a change

    B) encouraging the audience to think about the topic in a different way

    C) thinking about a topic or an idea in a different way

    D) changing or reinforcing attitudes, beliefs, and values

Answer: D
Page Ref: 354
Topic: Persuasion defined
Skill: Description Question

11) In the process of persuading your audience, the most difficult to change is your listeners'

    A) beliefs.   B) values.   C) emotions.   D) attitudes

Answer: B
Page Ref: 355
Topic: Persuasion defined
Skill: Description Question

12) You just listened to a persuasive speech and you were persuaded by the speaker. According to Aristotle and the Elaboration Likelihood Model of Persuasion (ELM) you were persuaded by

    A) ethos.   B) pathos.   C) logos.   D) credos.

Answer: C
Page Ref: 356
Topic: How persuasion works
Skill: Description Question

13) Sometimes persuasive messages using cognitive dissonance are so at odds with the listeners' attitudes, beliefs, and values that audiences

    A) may look elsewhere for information.   B) may discredit the source.

    C) may stop listening.   D) may reinterpret the message.

Answer: C
Page Ref: 357
Topic: How to motivate listeners
Skill: Description Question

14) Maslow's hierarchy of needs asserts that basic human needs must be satisfied before listeners can be motivated using any higher needs. These basic needs are

    A) physiological.   B) safety.   C) social.   D) psychological.

Answer: A
Page Ref: 360
Topic: Use listener needs
Skill: Description Question

15) When a proposition in a persuasive speech focuses on having the listener judge the work or importance of something, it is

    A) a proposition of fact.   B) a proposition of value.

    C) a proposition of policy.   D) a proposition of action.

Answer: B
Page Ref: 368
Topic: Develop your central idea and main ideas
Skill: Description Question

16) When a proposition in a persuasive speech focuses on changing a procedure, a law, or a behavior, it is

    A) a proposition of fact.   B) a proposition of value.

    C) a proposition of policy.   D) a proposition of action.

Answer: C
Page Ref: 368–369
Topic: Develop your central idea and main ideas
Skill: Description Question

17) If you present a pro-life speech and get the pro-choice listeners to feel uncomfortable with their positions, you have effectively used the persuasive technique of

    A) using negative motivation.   B) appealing to basic human needs.

    C) using emotional appeals.   D) using cognitive dissonance.

Answer: D
Page Ref: 357
Topic: How to motivate listeners
Skill: Example Question

18) When Jeri tries to persuade listeners to take action against corporations who pollute community waterways, she is appealing to

    A) listeners' security and safety needs.   B) listeners' physiological needs.

    C) listeners' social needs.   D) listeners' self-esteem needs.

Answer: B
Page Ref: 360
Topic: Use positive motivation
Skill: Example Question

19) Although Betsy lives in a state where carrying concealed weapons is legal, she wants to persuade her listeners that stricter handgun legislation should be passed. According to Maslow, which need is she addressing?

    A) physiological   B) safety   C) social   D) self-esteem

Answer: B
Page Ref: 360
Topic: Use listener needs
Skill: Example Question

20) Tiphani, in her persuasive speech, says the following: "So, by using these simple steps, you will save time, money, and energy." What form of persuasive appeal is this?

    A) an appeal to self-esteem needs   B) a negative or guilt-based appeal

    C) using cognitive dissonance   D) an appeal to positive motivation

Answer: D
Page Ref: 361
Topic: Use positive motivation
Skill: Example Question

21) Gina knew that many people were not in favor of gay marriage; however, in crafting her message she focused on the legal aspects of the recently passed state constitutional amendment and the possible negative impact on all residents of the state. According to the Social Judgment Theory, Gina was focused on the

    A) latitude of acceptance.   B) latitude of rejection.

    C) latitude of noncommitment.   D) latitude of progress.

Answer: B
Page Ref: 366
Topic: Determine your persuasive purpose
Skill: Example Question

22) The statement "Osama bin Laden was responsible for the September 11th tragedy," is a proposition of

    A) fact.   B) policy.   C) value.   D) attitude.

Answer: A
Page Ref: 367-368
Topic: Develop your central idea and main ideas
Skill: Example Question

23) In the Scott Peterson trial, his lawyers were attempting to prove he was not guilty of murdering his wife. In persuasion, this is known as

    A) a proposition of fact.   B) a proposition of value.

    C) a proposition of policy.   D) a proposition of action.

Answer: A
Page Ref: 367
Topic: Develop your central idea and main ideas
Skill: Example Question

24) Britt's central idea was to persuade her audience to volunteer one day a week at the homeless shelter. This persuasive speech was based on

    A) a proposition of fact.   B) a proposition of value.

    C) a proposition of policy.   D) a proposition of action.

Answer: C
Page Ref: 368-369
Topic: Develop your central idea and main ideas
Skill: Example Question

25) Lindsay decides to give a persuasive speech on the right to vote. She says that voting is important because it reveals one's patriotism while also upholding democracy in national, state, and local governments. Her statements most clearly reflect

    A) her values.   B) her attitudes.   C) her beliefs.   D) her facts.

Answer: A
Page Ref: 355
Topic: Persuasion defined
Skill: Application Question

26) Matt is listening to a persuasive speech on assisted suicide. He begins to feel uncomfortable but then decides the speaker didn't know what she was talking about. Matt is using which dissonance coping strategy?

    A) he is reinterpreting the message and restoring balance to what he is hearing

    B) he is discrediting the source

    C) he is using positive motivation to adjust to what he is hearing

    D) he is seeking new information

Answer: B
Page Ref: 358–359
Topic: How listeners cope with dissonance
Skill: Application Question

27) Lawanda just didn't want to change her stance on capital punishment, but Jack's argument did make her think twice about her position. However, instead of being persuaded, Lawanda dismissed the arguments by deeming Jack's facts unreliable. How has Lawanda responded to her own cognitive dissonance in this instance?

    A) by reinterpreting Jack's message

    B) by attacking the credibility of Jack's sources

    C) by simply refusing to listen to the remaining points

    D) by seeking information from another source

Answer: B
Page Ref: 358
Topic: Use dissonance
Skill: Application Question

28) Brendan argues, in his persuasive speech, "What starving people need first is food and clean water—not counseling about the sad state of their governments, not advice about ways to attract new industry, and not pity over the loss of their self-esteem." What principle of persuasive speaking is Brendan effectively utilizing?

    A) the principle of cognitive dissonance and negative motivation

    B) the principle of presenting more advantages than disadvantages

    C) the principle of creating gradual, rather than sudden, change in listeners

    D) the principle that basic needs must be satisfied before higher-level ones

Answer: D
Page Ref: 360
Topic: Use listener needs
Skill: Application Question

29) You want to do a speech on the importance of Yoga and an exercise routine, but you don't want to come across as though you were scolding the audience for not being more active. You simply want to uplift them, to make them feel good about their own potential, and to show them the health benefits of activity. If you do this, what persuasive strategy will you be using?

    A) positive motivation   B) negative motivation

    C) cognitive dissonance   D) fear appeals

Answer: A
Page Ref: 361
Topic: Use positive motivation
Skill: Application Question

30) In her persuasive speech, Martha spoke about the possibility of dirty nuclear weapons being used against the United States by Iraq, Iran, and North Korea. She challenged them to monitor Senate hearings on the problem and to get involved by writing or e-mailing their legislators. What form of motivation did Martha successfully employ in her speech?

    A) positive motivation, based on a patriotism appeal

    B) an appeal to basic self-esteem and self-actualization needs

    C) cognitive dissonance

    D) negative motivation, based on a fear appeal

Answer: D
Page Ref: 362-363
Topic: Use negative motivation
Skill: Application Question

31) Missy presented a persuasive speech on drunk driving. During the speech, she showed actual pictures of accidents that had been caused by drunk drivers. Some of the pictures were graphic and horrifying. Did Missy use motivation effectively?

A) Yes; fear appeals work well if they are used truthfully.

B) Yes; it is a good idea to use cognitive dissonance as persuasion.

C) No; graphic fear appeals will cause the listener to stop listening.

D) No; this form of cognitive dissonance is ineffectual.

Answer: C
Page Ref: 362
Topic: Negative motivation
Skill: Application Question

32) Janet saw on the news where a family of seven children perished in a house fire--it was also revealed that the house did not contain smoke detectors. As a result she developed a persuasive speech stating that this tragedy can be avoided in everyone's home with the simple installation of a smoke detector. Janet was using which kind of proposition as her central idea?

A) proposition of value   B) proposition of fact

C) proposition of policy   D) proposition of action

Answer: B
Page Ref: 366-367
Topic: Develop your central idea and main ideas
Skill: Application Question

33) Persuasive speeches ask audiences to make an explicit choice, rather than just informing them of their options.

Answer: TRUE
Page Ref: 354
Topic: Persuasion defined

34) Persuasion is the process of changing or reinforcing attitudes, beliefs, values, or behaviors.

Answer: TRUE
Page Ref: 355
Topic: Persuasion defined

35) Of attitudes, beliefs, and value, beliefs are the most easily changed.

Answer: FALSE
Page Ref: 355
Topic: Persuasion defined

36) A belief is a learned predisposition to respond favorably or unfavorably toward something.

Answer: FALSE
Page Ref: 355
Topic: Persuasion defined

37) Persistence is the underlying internal force that drives us to achieve our goals.

Answer: FALSE
Page Ref: 356
Topic: How persuasion works

38) If a persuasive speaker causes you to become uncomfortable with your own position or view on an issue, the speaker has successfully used a strategy known as cognitive dissonance.

Answer: TRUE
Page Ref: 357–358
Topic: How to motivate listeners

39) One common audience member response to cognitive dissonance is to simply stop listening to the speaker.

Answer: TRUE
Page Ref: 358–359
Topic: How listeners cope with dissonance

40) Fear appeals and negative motivation are more intimidating if they are directed toward the audience rather than a loved one of an individual.

Answer: FALSE
Page Ref: 362
Topic: Use negative motivation

41) Recent research indicates that there is a direct link to the intensity of the fear appeal and the likelihood that listeners will be persuaded by the message.

Answer: TRUE
Page Ref: 362
Topic: Use negative motivation

42) Latitude of acceptance, latitude of denial, and latitude of noncommunication are all part of Social Judgment Theory.

Answer: FALSE
Page Ref: 366
Topic: Determine your persuasive purpose

43) Give brief definitions for the following terms: attitudes, beliefs, values.
Page Ref: 355
Topic: Persuasion defined

44) What is cognitive dissonance? Explain how it can be used effectively to persuade.
Page Ref: 357–358
Topic: How to motivate listeners

45) Explain how to best use positive motivation in your persuasive message by appealing to your audience's values and needs.

   Page Ref: 361
   Topic: Use positive motivation

46) What is a proposition in persuasion? Name and give examples of the three types.

   Page Ref: 366–369
   Topic: Develop your central idea and main ideas

47) With a speech topic of your choosing, briefly define and explain the Social Judgment Theory concepts of latitude of acceptance, latitude of rejection, and latitude of noncommitment.

   Page Ref: 366
   Topic: Determine your persuasive purpose

48) In persuasive speaking, it is important to know exactly how to motivate your listeners. Your text explores four ways to motivate listeners to your persuasive message. Identify each and offer a brief explanation of how each can be used to motivate listeners.

   Page Ref: 357–363
   Topic: How to motivate listeners

49) Maslow's hierarchy is one of the most time-honored devices for helping speakers understand the principles behind persuasion. Either by drawing a diagram of the hierarchy and labeling its parts, or by explaining each level in a paragraph, demonstrate your understanding of how persuasion is related to basic needs.

   Page Ref: 360
   Topic: Use listener needs

50) Your text provides three types of propositions that serve as central ideas in a persuasive speech. Identify and explain each type. Then, using the hypothetical speech topic of "The War on Terrorism," write a proposition statement that reflects each of the three types.

   Page Ref: 366–369
   Topic: Develop your central idea and main ideas

Chapter 17 Using Persuasive Strategies

1) The audience's perception of a speaker's competence, trustworthiness, and dynamism is termed

    A) character.   B) credibility.   C) charisma.   D) personality.

Answer: B
Page Ref: 376
Topic: Enhancing your credibility
Skill: Definition Question

2) What is Aristotle's term for speaker credibility?

    A) logos   B) pathos   C) ethos   D) credos

Answer: C
Page Ref: 376
Topic: Enhancing your credibility
Skill: Definition Question

3) As a Roman teacher of public speaking, Quintilian felt that effective public speakers should be

    A) polished and prepared in the speaking situation.

    B) charismatic in all aspects of speaking.

    C) people of good character.

    D) trustworthy and loyal.

Answer: C
Page Ref: 376
Topic: Enhancing your credibility
Skill: Definition Question

4) The factor in a speaker's credibility that refers to his or her being perceived as energetic is known as

    A) competence.   B) trustworthiness.

    C) dynamism.   D) charisma.

Answer: C
Page Ref: 377
Topic: Enhancing your credibility
Skill: Definition Question

5) The type of credibility is established by giving careful thought to your appearance, establishing eye contact, and having your credentials as well as accomplishments presented to the audience.

A) initial credibility.

B) derived credibility.

C) terminal credibility.

D) deserved credibility.

Answer: A
Page Ref: 377
Topic: Enhancing your credibility
Skill: Definition Question

6) The term that Aristotle used to refer to using evidence and reasoning to reach a conclusion is

A) ethos.   B) pathos.   C) mythos.   D) logos.

Answer: D
Page Ref: 378
Topic: Using logic and evidence to persuade
Skill: Definition Question

7) The type of reasoning in which one thing, person, or process is compared to another to predict how something will perform or respond is

A) syllogism.   B) deduction.   C) induction.   D) analogy.

Answer: D
Page Ref: 380
Topic: Understanding types of reasoning
Skill: Definition Question

8) The term used by Aristotle to describe appeals to human emotion is

A) rhetoric.   B) ethos.   C) logos.   D) pathos.

Answer: D
Page Ref: 388
Topic: Tips for using emotion to persuade
Skill: Definition Question

9) A process of reasoning from a general statement or principle to reach a specific, certain conclusion is known as

A) inductive reasoning.

B) deductive reasoning.

C) reasoning by analogy.

D) generalization.

Answer: B
Page Ref: 381
Topic: Understanding types of reasoning
Skill: Description Question

10) A three-part way of developing an argument with a major premise, a minor premise, and a conclusion is known as

A) a generalization.
B) a syllogism.
C) an analogy.
D) causal reasoning.

Answer: B
Page Ref: 381
Topic: Understanding types of reasoning
Skill: Description Question

11) What is the term for a conclusion reached based on available evidence?

A) a fact
B) an example
C) an inference
D) an opinion

Answer: C
Page Ref: 385
Topic: Supporting reasoning with evidence
Skill: Description Question

12) What is testimony or quotations that express attitudes, beliefs, or values of someone else?

A) fact
B) inference
C) example
D) opinion

Answer: D
Page Ref: 385
Topic: Supporting reasoning with evidence
Skill: Description Question

13) When speakers attempt to persuade without adequate evidence or use arguments that are irrelevant or inappropriate, they are using

A) an opinion
B) a deduction
C) a fallacy
D) an inference

Answer: C
Page Ref: 386
Topic: Avoiding faulty reasoning: ethical issues
Skill: Description Question

14) Reasoning that suggests that because everyone else believes something or is doing something, then it must be valid, accurate, or effective is a

A) causal fallacy
B) bandwagon fallacy
C) hasty generalization
D) red herring

Answer: B
Page Ref: 386
Topic: Avoiding faulty reasoning: ethical issues
Skill: Description Question

15) When a persuasive speaker attacks the person supporting an issue rather than the issue itself, which fallacy is the speaker committing?

    A) non sequitur   B) hasty generalization

    C) ad hominem   D) bandwagon

Answer: C
Page Ref: 387
Topic: Avoiding faulty reasoning: ethical issues
Skill: Description Question

16) An emotional appeal that reaches the audience through shared beliefs based on cultural heritage or faith is known as

    A) hope.   B) reverence.   C) myth.   D) pride.

Answer: C
Page Ref: 392
Topic: Tips for using emotion to persuade
Skill: Description Question

17) What is the term for reasoning that uses specific instances of examples to reach a general, probable conclusion?

    A) probability   B) validity

    C) inductive reasoning   D) mythos

Answer: C
Page Ref: 379
Topic: Understanding types of reasoning
Skill: Definition Question

18) "All United States citizens have a First Amendment right to free speech. The members of the KKK are citizens of the United States. Therefore, the members of the KKK have a right to express their opinions" is an example of

    A) inductive reasoning.   B) deductive reasoning.

    C) causal reasoning.   D) ad hominem.

Answer: B
Page Ref: 381
Topic: Understanding types of reasoning
Skill: Example Question

19) Georgia argued that all people who commit murder should be punished. Further she stated that Farley committed second degree murder, thus concluding Farley should be punished. Georgia has used

    A) an inductive argument.   B) an enthymeme.

    C) a syllogism.   D) a causal argument.

Answer: C
Page Ref: 381
Topic: Understanding types of reasoning
Skill: Example Question

20) Tamara, when speaking to persuade the class that prayer in schools should be restored, argues, "The reason that there is so much crime and violence nowadays is that we no longer have prayer in schools and answer to a Higher authority," you recognize this fallacy as

    A) a red herring.   B) an ad hominem.

    C) either–or.   D) a causal fallacy.

Answer: D
Page Ref: 386
Topic: Avoiding faulty reasoning: ethical issues
Skill: Example Question

21) Shylah states in her persuasive speech, "Marijuana is a safe alternate to alcohol. I know this because most of my friends use it and they're fine." You recognize this fallacy as

    A) bandwagon.   B) ad hominem.   C) false cause.   D) red herring.

Answer: A
Page Ref: 386
Topic: Avoiding faulty reasoning: ethical issues
Skill: Example Question

22) When Nicole said, "My grandfather's test results were misread at the XYZ Medical Lab. As a result he received the wrong medicine and medical treatment. The XYZ Lab can not be trusted," you recognized this fallacy as

    A) a red herring.   B) an ad hominem.

    C) a bandwagon fallacy.   D) a hasty generalization.

Answer: D
Page Ref: 387
Topic: Avoiding faulty reasoning: ethical issues
Skill: Example Question

23) The textbook gives an example of a politician calling a press conference when he is being accused of taking bribes while in office. Instead of addressing this issue, the political speaks about the evils of child pornography. What fallacy is this politician practicing?

    A) red herring   B) appeal to misplaced authority

    C) hasty generalization   D) either/or

Answer: A
Page Ref: 386–387
Topic: Avoiding faulty reasoning: ethical issues
Skill: Example Question

24) In his persuasive speech, Phil referred to the "the horror of the 11th of September, 2001." You recognize this as an emotional appeal to his audience's shared experience or

    A) terror.   B) hope.   C) fear.   D) myth.

Answer: D
Page Ref: 392
Topic: Myth
Skill: Example Question

25) When Ramone spoke about the need for regular health check-ups, he was so knowledgeable, so sincere, and so energetic in his delivery that everyone responded quite positively to his speech. What aspect of good persuasive delivery did Ramone demonstrate?

   A) mythos   B) logos   C) pathos   D) ethos

Answer: D
Page Ref: 376
Topic: Enhancing your credibility
Skill: Application Question

26) In your speech to a group of high school students, you explain how you have seen people do stupid things at parties as a result of drinking, you've seen how drunk people put themselves at risk, and you've heard of people's reputations being ruined because of alcohol-related incidents. Because of what you've seen, you want to encourage your listeners to avoid drinking in social situations no matter the peer pressure. What form of reasoning have you used in this speech?

   A) deductive   B) inductive   C) causal   D) syllogistic

Answer: B
Page Ref: 379-380
Topic: Understanding types of reasoning
Skill: Application Question

27) In a speech to the neighborhood watch group, Mr. Simmons made the following statement: "If you see someone running down the sidewalk in our neighborhood and you don't recognize that person, you can assume that person has committed some type of crime. You must act immediately. Don't hesitate for a second. Call 911." Some members of the audience recognized this statement as an example of

   A) a causal fallacy.   B) causal reasoning.

   C) deductive reasoning.   D) a bandwagon fallacy.

Answer: A
Page Ref: 386
Topic: Avoiding faulty reasoning: ethical issues
Skill: Application Question

28) Marty's persuasive speech was about gun control and school violence. He made the statement, "Either we take guns out of the hands of everyone in this country, except the police and military, or we can expect massacres in schools all over this country." This kind of argument represents

   A) a bandwagon fallacy.   B) an ad hominem fallacy.

   C) an appeal to misplaced authority.   D) an either-or fallacy.

Answer: D
Page Ref: 386-387
Topic: Avoiding faulty reasoning: ethical issues
Skill: Application Question

29) In an introduction to a persuasive speech, Fran said: "There was a time when I thought I would never have a job, a decent life, a boyfriend, or any pleasure in life. But, after working as an intern at Channel 3, I know what I really want to do with my life and that gives me great satisfaction. I encourage you all to become interns, so that you, too, can discover that there is something in life that inspires passion in you... that you're willing to work for...to work hard for...to be successful...to be happy." What type of message did this speaker effectively use in this introduction?

A) an appeal to credibility

B) an appeal to reasoning

C) an appeal to emotion

D) an appeal to a common myth

Answer: C
Page Ref: 388–390
Topic: Using emotion to persuade
Skill: Application Question

30) During her speech on creating a healthier environment, Maureen stated that more laws should be in effect to protect the environment because her town had a littering problem. Maureen was demonstrating which fallacy?

A) casual fallacy   B) red herring   C) ad hominem   D) non sequitur

Answer: D
Page Ref: 386–388
Topic: Avoiding faulty reasoning: ethical issues
Skill: Application Question

31) As United Nations representatives, Shanthy and Miles were determined to establish an early warning system for tsunamic threats. They had personally seen the devastation to their homeland of Sri Lanka in December 2004, and knew they had the power to affect change. In their speeches before the UN, they showed heartbreaking pictures and the tragic amateur videos from those vacationing where the tsunami had struck. In the end, they were able to persuade the audience to consider the proposal for an early warning system. Which tip did they follow for using emotions to persuade?

A) They used emotion-arousing images to trigger audience response.

B) They used an appeal to evoke feelings of hope and pride.

C) They used concrete facts that appealed to the audience's logic.

D) They used an argument organized by problem and solution.

Answer: A
Page Ref: 390
Topic: Tips for using emotion to persuade
Skill: Application Question

32) In Montana's persuasive speech against assisted suicide, she quoted the Bible, saying, "Thou shalt not kill." What type of appeal was Montana using in this speech?

    A) an appeal to reason   B) an appeal to fear

    C) an appeal to myth   D) an appeal to credibility

Answer: C
Page Ref: 392
Topic: Tips for using emotion to persuade
Skill: Application Question

33) A speaker posing competence is one that is informed, skilled, and knowledgeable about the subject at topic.

Answer: TRUE
Page Ref: 376
Topic: Enhancing your credibility

34) A good speaker will establish eye contact with the audience before beginning the speech.

Answer: TRUE
Page Ref: 376
Topic: Enhancing your credibility

35) Derived credibility refers to that which a speaker achieves after presenting a speech.

Answer: FALSE
Page Ref: 377
Topic: Enhancing your credibility

36) Causal reasoning is making a faulty cause–and–effect connection between two things or events.

Answer: FALSE
Page Ref: 382–383
Topic: Understanding types of reasoning

37) In persuading an intercultural audience, remember that all cultures assume a direct, linear, methodical approach to supporting ideas and proving a point.

Answer: FALSE
Page Ref: 383
Topic: Persuading the diverse audience

38) A hypothetical example should not be used to reach a conclusion.

Answer: TRUE
Page Ref: 385
Topic: Supporting reasoning with evidence

39) An inference is a conclusion based on available evidence.

Answer: TRUE
Page Ref: 385
Topic: Supporting reasoning with evidence

40) One important step in persuading receptive audiences is to make it easy for them to take action.

Answer: TRUE
Page Ref: 394
Topic: Persuading the receptive audience

41) The five steps in the Motivated Sequence are: attention, need, satisfaction, example, and action.

Answer: FALSE
Page Ref: 399–403
Topic: Motivated sequence

42) Monroe's Motivated Sequence is a guide, not an absolute formula for persuasion.

Answer: TRUE
Page Ref: 399–403
Topic: Motivated sequence

43) List the four strategies for organizing persuasive messages and define them.

Page Ref: 397–403
Topic: Strategies for organizing persuasive messages

44) List five strategies for adapting ideas to people or people to ideas and demonstrate how each might be used in a speech.

Page Ref: 393–397
Topic: Strategies for adapting ideas to people and people to ideas

45) Give three examples of faulty reasoning in persuasion. Define and give an example of each.

Page Ref: 386–388
Topic: Avoiding faulty reasoning: ethical issues

46) What are three ways that emotional appeals can be effectively used in persuasion? Give an example of each.

Page Ref: 388–393
Topic: Using emotion to persuade

47) Briefly list and explain the points presented in the textbook on how to persuade an unreceptive audience.

Page Ref: 395–397
Topic: Persuading the unreceptive audience

48) Of the three main types of reasoning discussed in your text, select two and explain the main differences between them. Using the hypothetical topic "Abortion," construct an argument with each of the two selected.

Page Ref: 378–383
Topic: Using logic and evidence to persuade

49) Your textbook provides some excellent strategies for persuading different kinds of audiences. In a thorough, detailed essay, first identify the three types of audiences. Then provide and explain two strategies to enhance persuasion for each type of audience.

Page Ref: 393–397
Topic: Strategies for adapting ideas to people and people to ideas

50) Using the hypothetical speech topic "Donate Blood to Your Local Red Cross," develop an organizational plan using the motivated sequence. Make sure to include and explain each step in the sequence.

Page Ref: 399–403
Topic: The motivated sequence

Chapter 18 Special–Occasion Speaking

1) The most common oral presentation of information or policy made in and related to the workplace is known as

   A) a speech.   B) a meeting.   C) a brief.   D) a report.

Answer: D
Page Ref: 412
Topic: Public speaking in the workplace
Skill: Definition Question

2) These speeches are designed to inform the public, strengthen alliances with them, and possibly recommend policy to those outside the work environment.

   A) a persuasive presentation.   B) an organizational report.

   C) a public relations speech.   D) a news briefing.

Answer: C
Page Ref: 413
Topic: Public speaking in the workplace
Skill: Definition Question

3) A brief, accurate speech where the goals are to provide information and build another speaker's credibility is

   A) a speech of introduction.   B) a toast.

   C) a commemorative address.   D) an award presentation

Answer: A
Page Ref: 414
Topic: Ceremonial speaking
Skill: Definition Question

4) When offering a brief salute to a special occasion or person, you are giving

   A) a eulogy.   B) an address.

   C) a toast.   D) an introduction.

Answer: C
Page Ref: 415
Topic: Ceremonial speaking
Skill: Definition Question

5) A special-occasion speech given to mark an anniversary of a special event, the completion of a long task, or high achievement in some field.

   A) a toast.   B) an acceptance speech.

   C) a presentation speech.   D) a speech of tribute.

Answer: C
Page Ref: 416
Topic: Ceremonial speaking
Skill: Definition Question

6) The special-occasion speech, given at or near the beginning of a meeting or a conference, which sets the theme and tone is what kind of speech?

   A) a speech of introduction.   B) a tribute

   C) a keynote address   D) a report

   Answer: C
   Page Ref: 418-419
   Topic: Ceremonial speaking
   Skill: Definition Question

7) A phrase in which the initial sounds of words are switched is known as

   A) a pun.   B) a spoonerism.   C) a malapropism.   D) hyperbole.

   Answer: B
   Page Ref: 422
   Topic: After-dinner speaking: using humor effectively
   Skill: Definition Question

8) The mistaken use of a word that sounds much like the intended word, such as "infatuation" for "inflation", is known as

   A) verbal irony.   B) a spoonerism.

   C) a malapropism.   D) understatement.

   Answer: C
   Page Ref: 422
   Topic: After-dinner speaking: using humor effectively
   Skill: Definition Question

9) When presenting a report in your workplace, your general purpose is

   A) to use presentation aids to clarify your points.

   B) to communicate information or policy.

   C) to be thorough so there are no questions afterward.

   D) to impress your boss with how smart you are.

   Answer: B
   Page Ref: 412
   Topic: Public speaking in the workplace
   Skill: Description Question

10) In a public relations presentation, the speaker should anticipate and prepare for criticism by

   A) defending the position of his organization.

   B) ignoring any objections, just remain positive.

   C) explaining more carefully the organization's plan.

   D) planning to counter objections and problems.

   Answer: D
   Page Ref: 413
   Topic: Public speaking in the workplace
   Skill: Description Question

11) What two criteria are most important when making a speech of introduction?

    A) Be brief and witty.   B) Be brief and informative.

    C) Be brief and accurate.   D) Be accurate and self-serving.

Answer: C
Page Ref: 414-415
Topic: Ceremonial speaking
Skill: Description Question

12) When called upon to give an impromptu toast at a wedding,

    A) tell a joke about unhappy marriages and divorce.

    B) tell a long, detailed story about the bride and groom.

    C) raise your glass and say, "Bottoms up!"

    D) let those gathered and the occasion dictate what you say.

Answer: D
Page Ref: 415-416
Topic: Ceremonial speaking
Skill: Description Question

13) When you make a speech placing someone's name in nomination for an office or award, what should you be sure to mention?

    A) the history and significance of the award or office

    B) past winners or office-holders who are in the audience

    C) funny stories that might be associated with the nominee

    D) the nominee's qualifications for this award or office

Answer: D
Page Ref: 417
Topic: Ceremonial speaking
Skill: Description Question

14) What should the speaker keep in mind when giving an acceptance speech?

    A) Use an impromptu delivery so the remarks don't sound canned.

    B) Thank those giving your the award and comment on the significance of the award to you.

    C) Be emotional, be sincere, and take as long as you wish.

    D) Write out your whole speech, word-for-word on note cards, so you can use them to read from.

Answer: B
Page Ref: 417-418
Topic: Ceremonial speaking
Skill: Description Question

15) The speaker talking about recycling said, "I took a beer bottle to the recycling center, but they wouldn't take it. They said: 'This is the **pint** of no return.'" What humorous verbal strategy did the speaker engage in?

A) a pun. B) a spoonerism. C) a malapropism. D) hyperbole.

Answer: A
Page Ref: 422
Topic: After-dinner speaking: using humor effectively
Skill: Description Question

16) Comedian Henny Youngman once said, "I've got all the money I'll ever need--if I die by four o'clock." Why would this be an example of a witty saying?

A) The final part of his quotation catches the audience off guard.

B) He's saying just the opposite of what he really means.

C) It's an exaggeration.

D) He uses a double meaning to create humor.

Answer: A
Page Ref: 423
Topic: After-dinner speaking: using humor effectively
Skill: Description Question

17) Routine summaries at meetings, reports to the board, sales pitches to clients, and training seminars for coworkers are all examples of

A) public relations speeches. B) informative speeches.

C) workplace public speaking. D) ceremonial public speaking.

Answer: C
Page Ref: 412
Topic: Public speaking in the workplace
Skill: Example Question

18) At the monthly meeting of the Chamber of Commerce, a representative from a local tour bus company makes a presentation about the economic advantages for using her company's services for visiting dignitaries. What kind of special-occasion speech is this?

A) a public relations speech B) a professional report

C) a keynote address D) a ceremonial speech

Answer: A
Page Ref: 413-414
Topic: Public speaking in the workplace
Skill: Example Question

19) Martina is concerned about her introductory speech for the guest speaker at her banquet. According to your textbook, what should Martina keep in mind?

    A) Audiences don't usually listen to introductions of speakers.

    B) She should mention why she was chosen for this honor.

    C) She should introduce the topic and the speaker, briefly and accurately.

    D) She should tell as much about the speaker's credentials as she can find.

    Answer: C
    Page Ref: 414–415
    Topic: Ceremonial speaking
    Skill: Example Question

20) As maid of honor, Rhonda's toast at her best friend's wedding was as follows: "To the best girlfriend that ever graced my hometown, the best person to cry with, to laugh with, and to be happy with, on her happiest day; I wish you both all the best." Was this effective, according to the criteria discussed in the chapter on special-occasion speaking?

    A) No, because it was not funny.   B) Yes, because it was sincere.

    C) Yes, because it was funny.   D) No, because it was too personal.

    Answer: B
    Page Ref: 415–416
    Topic: Ceremonial speaking
    Skill: Example Question

21) Renton has been asked to present his colleague, Rebecca, with the "Journalist of the Year" award. What is important for him to remember to say in this speech?

    A) to quickly announce the recipient's name and let her talk about the award

    B) to talk about the last recipient of the award and his accomplishments

    C) to briefly refer to the occasion and mention the significance of the award

    D) to mention that his colleague has been up for this award twice before

    Answer: C
    Page Ref: 416–417
    Topic: Ceremonial speaking
    Skill: Example Question

22) In her keynote speech for a real estate convention in town, Joanna decided to announce her candidacy for mayor of the city. Her speech consisted mainly of her stances on various campaign issues. Was this appropriate for a keynote speech?

   A) No; Joanna forgot that a keynote address should include the historical background of the organization.

   B) No; Joanna's keynote address should stress the topic or purpose of the meeting and set a theme or tone.

   C) Yes; Joanna is an important person in her town, and the announcement for her candidacy was suitable.

   D) Yes; Joanna knows there are no strict rules or guidelines about the content of a keynote address.

Answer: B
Page Ref: 418-419
Topic: Ceremonial speaking
Skill: Example Question

23) On the first anniversary of Ronald Reagan's death, the Reagan family and a group of close friends gathered at the Reagan Library to talk about Ronald Reagan's life and accomplishments. Then former President George H. W. Bush gave a brief speech at the occasion. What is the textbook term for this speech?

   A) a presentation speech   B) a commencement address

   C) a speech of dedication   D) a commemorative address

Answer: D
Page Ref: 420
Topic: Ceremonial speaking
Skill: Example Question

24) You have been asked to present an after-dinner speech to a local organization; something lighthearted and funny. You're not a naturally funny person, so this request unnerves you. What should you do?

   A) Remember to relate to the audience, use simple humorous stories, have a broad repertoire of stories, and know your information well.

   B) Use one of Dave Barry's old after-dinner speeches and tailor it to the occasion; he's always funny.

   C) Consult humorous sources and joke books and just tell a series of jokes.

   D) Turn down the invitation, explaining you don't have a sense of humor and wouldn't want to embarrass yourself.

Answer: A
Page Ref: 421-422
Topic: After-dinner speaking: using humor effectively
Skill: Example Question

25) When Jonathan began his report to the company vice-presidents, he acknowledged the reason why everyone was there. He then explained how he gathered the information he was to share with the group. Was this a good beginning, according to your text?

    A) No; Jonathan has already made two mistakes in this presentation.

    B) No; Jonathan wasted valuable time by acknowledging something everyone already knew.

    C) Yes; Jonathan demonstrated the first two guidelines related to presenting reports.

    D) Yes; but only if Jonathan gets to the heart of the matter quickly—the outcomes or solutions.

Answer: C
Page Ref: 412
Topic: Public speaking in the workplace
Skill: Application Question

26) Heather has been invited to speak to her daughter's fifth-grade class about her profession. Should Heather approach this presentation somewhat like she would a report? What is the best advice for Heather, in meeting this challenge?

    A) Treat the presentation like a report, but get to the solutions part early to keep the kids listening.

    B) Treat the presentation as a public relations speech, but adjust the language and technical level.

    C) Pick a topic and try to teach the class something new, just as their teacher would.

    D) Begin by saying, "Most of you know that I'm Mia's Momma. She made me come. Ha Ha."

Answer: B
Page Ref: 413-414
Topic: Public speaking in the workplace
Skill: Application Question

27) When Keith gave his speech of introduction about an associate who was to be the main dinner speaker, Keith told a story about the colleague getting drunk at a ball game and yelling at the umpire. According to your textbook information on how to give a speech of introduction, did Keith do the right thing?

    A) Yes; an introducer should give humorous insights into the character of the next speaker.

    B) Yes; the story relaxed everyone and made them ready to listen to the main speaker.

    C) No; the introducer should emphasize the credibility of the main speaker, not poke fun.

    D) No; the introducer's main responsibility is to overview what the main speaker will discuss.

Answer: C
Page Ref: 414-415
Topic: Ceremonial speaking
Skill: Application Question

28) At his best friend's wedding, Daniel gave a long toast in which he told funny stories about high school days, past romances—including broken hearts, and his first impressions of his best friend's new bride. Was this appropriate, according to your textbook advice on giving a toast?

   A) Yes; the text advises to try to use humor when making a toast.

   B) Yes; it is a tradition at American weddings for the best man to try to embarrass the groom.

   C) No; this toast was inappropriate because it was personal and it focused too much on the groom.

   D) No; toasts should be brief and appropriate for the audience and the occasion.

Answer: D
Page Ref: 415-416
Topic: Ceremonial speaking
Skill: Application Question

29) Marianne was so blown away by the announcement that she had won an award that she felt numb on her way to accept it. When she got to the microphone, she began to ramble and then thanked everyone she could think of for voting for her and supporting her. The speech ran several minutes long and had no organization. Is this appropriate for an acceptance speech?

   A) Yes; award-winners can take lots of time to thank everyone who encouraged and assisted them.

   B) Yes; there are no expectations that award acceptance speeches will be brief and organized.

   C) No; impromptu acceptance speeches should be brief, gracious, and as organized as possible.

   D) No; award-winners are expected to prepare brief remarks in advance of the presentation.

Answer: C
Page Ref: 417-418
Topic: Ceremonial speaking
Skill: Application Question

30) A renowned philanthropist and well-respected national speaker gave the commencement address at Audrey's graduation ceremony. He spoke of his concerns about rising crime rates for juveniles, of the problem of gang violence, and about crimes against women. Was this appropriate content for a commencement address?

   A) No; he should have treated the event like an after-dinner speech—a speech to entertain.

   B) No; because he didn't praise, inspire, or challenge the graduating class.

   C) Yes; because it dealt with serious concerns that will continue to face the graduates.

   D) Yes; because his approach was different and commencement addresses often become boring.

Answer: B
Page Ref: 419-420
Topic: Ceremonial speaking
Skill: Application Question

31) Godfrey was asked to be the commencement speaker at the local high school. In the speech Godfrey talked about his accomplishments, what he has been doing since his high school graduation 20 years ago, and his goals for the future. Unfortunately, this speech didn't appeal to the audience. Why?

    A) The audience really didn't get to know Godfrey because the speech was too short.

    B) Godfrey connected with the audience, but the illustrations he used were dated.

    C) The speech Godfrey gave was at the beginning of the commencement and set the tone for the event.

    D) Godfrey didn't praise the graduating class or have the graduates look toward their own futures.

Answer: D
Page Ref: 419-420
Topic: Ceremonial speaking
Skill: Application Question

32) At Donald's funeral, Patrick was asked to give the eulogy. In the eulogy, Patrick mentioned Donald's accomplishments in art, his loving devotion to his family, and how Donald got people to smile with the short stories or jokes he told--he always had people laughing. At the close of the eulogy, Patrick encouraged everyone to keep Donald in their memories and close to their heart. What guidelines did Patrick follow in preparing this eulogy?

    A) Remember to mention the achievements of the person who has died and take as much time as necessary to present these ideas.

    B) Remember to present all the facts and ideas clearly and do so with little emotion so the family and friends gathered will no be upset further by their loss.

    C) Remember the achievements of the person, include personal recollections, and encourage those assembled to move beyond their sorrow.

    D) Remember to list all the accomplishments of the person and briefly discuss the personal life of the person who has dies.

Answer: C
Page Ref: 420-421
Topic: Ceremonial speaking
Skill: Application Question

33) The primary purpose of a workplace report is to inform the public about one's company and to improve connections with the public.

Answer: FALSE
Page Ref: 412
Topic: Public speaking in the workplace

34) When giving a public relations speech, you should anticipate objections in the minds of your listeners and answer those objections in your speech.

Answer: TRUE
Page Ref: 413
Topic: Public speaking in the workplace

35) If a speaker needs no introduction, you should present one anyway.

Answer: FALSE
Page Ref: 414-415
Topic: Ceremonial speaking

36) The origin of the word "toast" comes from the Victorian practice of throwing bread at the bride and groom.

Answer: FALSE
Page Ref: 415-416
Topic: Ceremonial speaking

37) The three necessary elements for an award-presentation speech are a reference to the occasion, a brief history of the award and its significance, and the naming of the awardee.

Answer: TRUE
Page Ref: 416-417
Topic: Ceremonial speaking

38) The first part of an acceptance speech should be to thank the person making the presentation and the organization that person represents; then, mention a few of the people responsible for your success.

Answer: TRUE
Page Ref: 417-418
Topic: Ceremonial speaking

39) The keynote speaker at a conference should mention all the other speakers that will follow.

Answer: FALSE
Page Ref: 418-419
Topic: Ceremonial speaking

40) The speeches given at graduation ceremonies are known as commemorative addresses.

Answer: FALSE
Page Ref: 419-420
Topic: Ceremonial speaking

41) Some humor may be appropriate in a eulogy or speech of tribute to someone who died.

Answer: TRUE
Page Ref: 420-421
Topic: Ceremonial speaking

42) If you say "dalk the wog" instead of "walk the dog" you have engaged in the humorous verbal strategy of a spoonerism.

Answer: TRUE
Page Ref: 422
Topic: After-dinner speaking: using humor effectively

43) Identify the two types of work-related public speaking explained in your text. Then select one type and explain how it functions in a work setting.

   Page Ref: 412-414
   Topic: Public speaking in the workplace

44) Your job is to introduce a guest speaker for your organization. Using a real person of your choosing, write an introduction that will fulfill all the requirements of an introductory speech.

   Page Ref: 414-415
   Topic: Ceremonial speaking

45) Imagine you're at a family member's or your best friend's wedding, and it's come time for you to give a toast. In a brief essay, draft three toasts that would be appropriate for this occasion.

   Page Ref: 415-416
   Topic: Ceremonial speaking

46) What is the speaker's main purpose in each of the following special-occasion speeches: (1) a keynote address; (2) a commencement speech; and (3) a commemorative address?

   Page Ref: 418-419
   Topic: Ceremonial speaking

47) In an after-dinner speech, the speaker can use a play on words, hyperbole, understatement, verbal irony, or wit. Briefly define each one and give an example.

   Page Ref: 422-423
   Topic: After-dinner speaking: using humor effectively

48) In a well-developed essay, explain the importance of developing effective public speaking skills for the workplace. Identify two types of common workplace presentations, explaining the general function of each type.

   Page Ref: 412-414
   Topic: Public speaking in the workplace

49) At your graduation ceremony, a speaker will present a commencement address. Ideally, what would you like for the speaker to say to you upon graduation. Be specific, and include necessary functions of this type of speech as discussed in your text.

   Page Ref: 419-420
   Topic: Ceremonial speaking

50) A eulogy is one of the most difficult types of ceremonial speeches to present. Write a eulogy as you would like to have it presented at your own funeral. Be sure to include the elements, as described in your text, for an effective eulogy.

   Page Ref: 420-421
   Topic: Ceremonial speaking

Chapter 19 Speaking in Small Groups

1) Interaction between three to twelve people who share a common goal, a sense of commitment, and who attempt to influence one another is known as

   A) rhetorical communication.   B) personal communication.

   C) small group communication.   D) business communication.

   Answer: C
   Page Ref: 430
   Topic: Small group communication
   Skill: Definition Question

2) A coordinated small group of people organized to work together, with clearly defined roles and responsibilities, explicit rules, and well-defined goals is defined by your text as

   A) a team.   B) a consensus.

   C) a committee.   D) an organization.

   Answer: A
   Page Ref: 431
   Topic: Solving problems in groups and teams
   Skill: Definition Question

3) John Dewey's five step process of problem solving is known as

   A) Dewey's method.   B) problem-solution.

   C) scientific thinking.   D) reflective thinking.

   Answer: D
   Page Ref: 431
   Topic: Solving problems in groups and teams
   Skill: Definition Question

4) When working to solve a problem, one must set standards for identifying an acceptable solution. These standards are also known as

   A) analysis.   B) criteria.   C) items.   D) rules.

   Answer: B
   Page Ref: 432
   Topic: Solving problems in groups and teams
   Skill: Definition Question

5) When a group agrees to support and commit to the decision of the group, they have reached

   A) a solution.   B) a decision.   C) a consensus.   D) a census.

   Answer: C
   Page Ref: 434
   Topic: Solving problems in groups and teams
   Skill: Definition Question

6) The process of influencing others through communication is
    A) leadership.   B) persuasion.
    C) coercive.   D) time consuming.

    Answer: A
    Page Ref: 436
    Topic: Leading in small groups
    Skill: Definition Question

7) A group leader who assumes positions of superiority, giving orders and assuming control with
    a high degree of efficiency and little uncertainty is
    A) an authoritarian leader.   B) a democratic leader.
    C) a transformational leader.   D) a laissez faire leader.

    Answer: A
    Page Ref: 436
    Topic: Leading in small groups
    Skill: Definition Question

8) The process of influencing others by building a shared vision of the future, inspiring others to
    achieve, developing quality individual relationships with others, and helping people see how
    what they do is related to a larger framework is
    A) authoritarian leadership.   B) democratic leadership.
    C) transformational leadership.   D) laissez faire leadership.

    Answer: C
    Page Ref: 437
    Topic: Leading in small groups
    Skill: Definition Question

9) A group leader who is objective, encourages group discussions and decisions, and guides
    when necessary is
    A) an authoritarian leader.   B) a democratic leader.
    C) a transformational leader.   D) a laissez faire leader.

    Answer: B
    Page Ref: 436
    Topic: Leading in small groups
    Skill: Description Question

10) To be an effective meeting there should be a balance between two characteristics:
    A) evidence and evaluation.   B) leadership and followers.
    C) goals and accomplishments.   D) structure and interaction.

    Answer: D
    Page Ref: 438-439
    Topic: Managing meetings
    Skill: Description Question

11) The two most important things you can do to ensure that a meeting has appropriate structure is to identify the goals of the meeting, and the second is

    A) having the minutes from the previous meetings.

    B) developing an agenda for the meeting.

    C) using a space big enough to accommodate the members of the group.

    D) watching that the meeting stays within the established time limit.

Answer: B
Page Ref: 439
Topic: How to give meetings structure
Skill: Description Question

12) In a small group, the written description of the items and issues that will be discussed at a designated meeting is known as

    A) an agenda.   B) the list.   C) an order.   D) new business.

Answer: A
Page Ref: 439
Topic: Agenda
Skill: Description Question

13) The most important thing to do to ensure a meeting has appropriate structure is to first:

    A) set an agenda   B) take action

    C) identify the goals   D) make sure everyone is present

Answer: C
Page Ref: 439
Topic: How to give meetings structure
Skill: Description Question

14) A public discussion with a moderator in which a series of short speeches is presented to an audience is

    A) a symposium presentation.   B) a forum presentation.

    C) a panel discussion.   D) a group discussion.

Answer: A
Page Ref: 442
Topic: Presenting group recommendations
Skill: Description Question

15) In this type of group presentation, the format calls for audience members to direct questions and comments to a group who respond with short, impromptu speeches.

    A) a forum presentation   B) a symposium presentation.

    C) a panel discussion.   D) an office meeting.

Answer: A
Page Ref: 442
Topic: Presenting group recommendations
Skill: Description Question

16) According to your text, when making a group presentation the group members should do all of the following EXCEPT

    A) clarifying your purpose.

    B) using presentation aids effectively.

    C) assign someone to serve as coordinator or moderator.

    D) disregard time limits because of the number of members presenting information.

Answer: D
Page Ref: 444
Topic: Making a group presentation
Skill: Description Question

17) The group got together at Anita's apartment to work out a problem. First they made sure everyone had a clear sense of what the problem was; then they began to analyze it. What is going on in this group situation?

    A) Group members are effectively going through the decision-making process.

    B) Group members are effectively applying the problem-solution method to solve the problem.

    C) Group members are effectively applying the critical thinking method to the problem.

    D) Group members are effectively going through the reflective thinking process.

Answer: D
Page Ref: 431
Topic: Solving problems in groups and teams
Skill: Example Question

18) Lizzy realized that the group had been working on the problem for over 2 hours. At that point she recapped what the problem was, looked at the evidence that had been presented to that point, and suggested that the group stay on topic since they had drifted a couple time. Which tip for participating in a small group did Lizzy effectively enact?

    A) Prepare for group discussions.   B) Summarize the group's progress.

    C) Help manage conflict.   D) Evaluate the evidence.

Answer: B
Page Ref: 435
Topic: Participating in small groups
Skill: Example Question

19) You are new to the group, but you notice that the leader gives the group complete freedom in making decisions, gives various materials for the group to consider, but offers no feedback or direction to the group. This leadership style would be

    A) transformational leadership   B) democratic leadership

    C) authoritarian leadership   D) laissez faire leadership

Answer: D
Page Ref: 436–437
Topic: Leading small groups
Skill: Example Question

20) The instructor assigned Jan to be the group's leader, but others in the group have come to resent her. She rarely lets other group members offer suggestions and always controls how much gets accomplished. What's the term for Jan's leadership style?

   A) democratic   B) laissez faire   C) authoritarian   D) participative

   Answer: C
   Page Ref: 436-437
   Topic: Leading small groups
   Skill: Example Question

21) Of the various leadership roles that one can have in groups or teams, the role of the person who spurs the group on to action and productivity is known as

   A) the gatekeeper.   B) the elaborator.   C) the energizer.   D) the initiator.

   Answer: C
   Page Ref: 437
   Topic: Table 19.1, Leadership roles in groups and teams
   Skill: Example Question

22) In your office meetings, Lynda is the one who mediates disagreements that occur between the different group members. According to your text, what is the name of her leadership role in group maintenance?

   A) the encourager   B) the harmonizer
   C) the compromiser   D) the gatekeeper

   Answer: B
   Page Ref: 437
   Topic: Table 19.1, Leadership roles in groups and teams
   Skill: Example Question

23) Benita is an excellent group member. At meetings, she always shares her research with other group members. Which task-oriented role does Benita play, from this description?

   A) the elaborator   B) the information-seeker
   C) the information-giver   D) the opinion-giver

   Answer: C
   Page Ref: 437
   Topic: Table 19.1, Leadership roles in groups and teams
   Skill: Example Question

24) Hack detested going to group meetings because they were disorganized, conflict-oriented, and generally a waste of time. What simple device would help this group?

   A) a better leader   B) a meeting agenda
   C) disbanding the group   D) presentation aids

   Answer: B
   Page Ref: 439
   Topic: Managing meetings
   Skill: Example Question

25) Your group has thoroughly discussed the problem; now they are starting to generate possible solutions. However, they are getting bogged down by comments for or against certain ideas. What advice offered in the text would help your group in this situation?

   A) They should back up and make sure that everyone clearly understands the problem.

   B) They should write down the pros and cons of each idea, to keep the information organized.

   C) They should simply vote on which solution is the most feasible.

   D) They should refrain from criticizing ideas until they have generated a full list.

   Answer: D
   Page Ref: 431–432
   Topic: Solving problems in groups and teams
   Skill: Application Question

26) Mary Anne's group has been working hard and has now come up with several solutions to their problem. At this point, Mary Anne says, "Let's just list these and vote on the best one. It's the democratic way." What step has Mary Anne overlooked in the problem-solving process?

   A) She forgot to have the group identify any other possible solutions.

   B) She forgot to have the group consider the pros and cons of each solution.

   C) She forgot to have the group set up criteria for solving the problem.

   D) She forgot to have the group summarize all the problems suggested.

   Answer: B
   Page Ref: 434–435
   Topic: Participating in small groups
   Skill: Application Question

27) Group members are generating ideas at rapid speed and the problem-solving process is clipping right along when suddenly Rupert blurts out, "Can we stop and examine our evidence?" By saying this Rupert is

   A) helping the group evaluate its evidence

   B) introducing conflict into the group process.

   C) helping the group to manage conflict.

   D) showing that he has come prepared.

   Answer: A
   Page Ref: 435
   Topic: Participating in small groups
   Skill: Application Question

28) *Of Mice and Men* is more a description of what goes on in Ben's group meetings rather than the title of a classic book. When his group gets together to work on their class project, Ben and two other members do most of the talking. The other two members just sit there, letting the rest of the group carry them. What kind of maintenance role would help here?

   A) the compromiser   B) the harmonizer

   C) the encourager   D) the gatekeeper

   Answer: D
   Page Ref: 437
   Topic: Table 19.1, Leadership roles in groups and teams
   Skill: Application Question

29) Gloria prides herself on her leadership capabilities. In preparation for group meetings, Gloria makes sure the group is aware of a meeting's agenda, determines times and places for meetings, and gets useful information to members in advance of meetings. She also takes notes of what goes on at meetings. Is Gloria acting appropriately as group leader?

   A) No; she's doing too much when she should learn to farm out the work to group members.

   B) Yes; she's exhibiting several excellent leadership skills that are appropriate to her role.

   C) No; she really shouldn't be responsible for taking notes of what goes on at meetings.

   D) Yes; but what Gloria's doing should be expected of all group members, not just the leader.

   Answer: B
   Page Ref: 436–437
   Topic: Leading small groups
   Skill: Application Question

30) According to members of Lee's unit at work, Lee is an excellent manager. He knows what has to be done, gives his people clear orders, stays in the present rather than always dreaming about the future, and generally directs people with skill. What type of leadership style is most descriptive of Lee?

   A) laissez faire   B) transformational

   C) authoritarian   D) democratic

   Answer: C
   Page Ref: 436
   Topic: Leading small groups
   Skill: Application Question

31) Ed was one of those people who liked to make his presence known in group meetings. He never failed to offer an opinion or comment, even when it was obvious he didn't know anything about what was being discussed. Which recommendation about fostering group interaction should Ed be reminded of, in order to enhance group progress and satisfaction?

   A) Organize your contributions and make one point at a time.

   B) Speak only if your contribution is relevant.

   C) Listen actively and monitor your nonverbal communication.

   D) Speak only when spoken to by the group's leader.

Answer: B
Page Ref: 438–439
Topic: Managing meetings
Skill: Application Question

32) Christy was the moderator for a symposium presentation on "Gender Bias in the Workplace." After each member had spoken, the floor was open for questions. Paul stood up and asked Christy, "I have worked in this organization for 25 years and have seen marked improvement in the workplace. Why do we need to discuss this topic yet again? Aren't we beating a dead horse?" How should Christy respond?

   A) "If you can't ask questions in a more respectful way. I can't answer."

   B) "Because you're a man, you can't possibly understand our problem."

   C) "I'm sorry. I couldn't hear that question. Does anyone else have a question?"

   D) "I believe you'd like to know, briefly, why this is an important topic. Well..."

Answer: D
Page Ref: 441–442
Topic: Presenting group recommendations
Skill: Application Question

33) In problem solving, a group and a team are essentially the same thing.

Answer: FALSE
Page Ref: 430–431
Topic: Solving problems in groups and teams

34) Reflective thinking is John Dewey's five step method of problem solving.

Answer: TRUE
Page Ref: 431
Topic: Solving problems in groups and teams

35) Once a group has selected the best solution, their final task is to test and implement the solution.

Answer: TRUE
Page Ref: 433
Topic: Solving problems in groups and teams

36) Transformational leadership is the same thing as democratic leadership.

Answer: FALSE
Page Ref: 437
Topic: Solving problems in groups and teams

37) A good way to organize an agenda for a meeting is to save the most important items for last.

Answer: FALSE
Page Ref: 439
Topic: Managing meetings

38) A group leader should draw out quiet members by calling them by name and asking for their opinions.

Answer: TRUE
Page Ref: 440
Topic: Managing meetings

39) In a symposium presentation, it is not necessary to have a moderator.

Answer: FALSE
Page Ref: 442
Topic: Making a group presentation

40) A panel discussion is designed to inform an audience about issues, a problem, or to make recommendations.

Answer: TRUE
Page Ref: 442–443
Topic: Presenting group recommendations

41) When making a group presentation, it is helpful for the first speaker to clarify the group's purpose for the audience.

Answer: TRUE
Page Ref: 444
Topic: Making a group presentation

42) Presentation aids just get in the way when making a group presentation.

Answer: FALSE
Page Ref: 444
Topic: Making a group presentation

43) Identify the five steps that constitute John Dewey's reflective thinking process.
Page Ref: 431
Topic: Solving problems in groups and teams

44) Compare and contrast the following three types of leadership styles: (1) authoritarian; (2) democratic; and (3) laissez faire.

Page Ref: 436–437
Topic: Leading small groups

45) What are three recommendations for fostering group interaction, and how can they positively affect a group's productivity?

Page Ref: 440--441
Topic: Managing meetings

46) There are three primary presentation formats which exist for sharing recommendations with an audience. List and briefly explain each format.

Page Ref: 442–443
Topic: Presenting group recommendations

47) List and discuss four tips for making a good group presentation.

Page Ref: 444
Topic: Making a group presentation

48) Using the five steps listed in your text for group analysis of a problem, discuss each step with the hypothetical problem, "How can we solve the problem of teacher shortage in the public schools?"

Page Ref: 431–434
Topic: Solving problems in groups and teams

49) Within the reflective thinking process, step three is to generate possible solutions. Your text provides four guidelines for maximizing the effectiveness of this step. In a well-developed essay, identify and discuss these four guidelines, in terms of the benefits a group will derive if the guidelines are followed.

Page Ref: 431–434
Topic: Solving problems in groups and teams

50) When planning a group presentation, there are several things to keep in mind. Identify and discuss five guidelines, from the eight offered in your text, in terms of how they can make a presentation more successful.

Page Ref: 443–444
Topic: Planning a group presentation